This new book, the first from Beebe's pen since 1928, is a brilliant word picture of Nonsuch itself, "Land of Water", a sea-encompassed cedar-covered gem. On Nonsuch Island, Bermuda, Beebe and his scientific group have had their headquarters for three intensely interesting seasons. And it is of Nonsuch, and his work there, that Beebe writes. Some of the chapter headings attest the book's fine flavor: Mount Bermuda; the Cedars of Nonsuch; Battlefield of the Shore; Slicking for Flying Fish; Two Citizen Crabs of Nonsuch; a Motherly Knight in Armor.

Beebe has consorted with sea lions on the shores of the Galapagos; he has stalked the elusive Sargasso Sea, adventured with head-hunting Dyaks, studied rare creatures amid tropical tangles of orchids and ferns in South America, and plumbed record depths in his Bathysphere off Bermuda—and the color of these far-flung experiences lights the pages that he writes.

"Nonsuch" has much of the lure—literary and scientific—of that rare masterpiece of earlier years, "Jungle Peace".

NONSUCH:

Land of Water

William Beebe

BOOKS BY WILLIAM BEEBE

TWO BIRD-LOVERS IN MEXICO — *1905*

THE BIRD — *1906*

THE LOG OF THE SUN — *1906*

OUR SEARCH FOR A WILDERNESS — *1910*

TROPICAL WILD LIFE — *1917*

JUNGLE PEACE — *1918*

EDGE OF THE JUNGLE — *1921*

A MONOGRAPH OF THE PHEASANTS — *1918–1922*

GALÁPAGOS: WORLD'S END — *1924*

JUNGLE DAYS — *1925*

THE ARCTURUS ADVENTURE — *1926*

PHEASANTS: THEIR LIVES AND HOMES — *1926*

PHEASANT JUNGLES — *1927*

BENEATH TROPIC SEAS — *1928*

NONSUCH: LAND OF WATER — *1932*

Painting by Helen Tee-Van.

Many-colored Butterflyingfish.

Upper two figures — *Exonautes nonsuchae* Beebe and Tee-Van
Lower two figures — *Exonautes rondeletii* (C and V)

NONSUCH:
Land of Water

By

WILLIAM BEEBE, Sc.D., LL.D.

*Director of the Department of Tropical Research
of the New York Zoological Society.*

With 55 Illustrations

Published
Under the Auspices
of the
NEW YORK ZOOLOGICAL SOCIETY

BREWER, WARREN & PUTNAM
NEW YORK · 1932

TO

MONA WILLIAMS

ACKNOWLEDGMENTS

Chapters I and II were published in the Atlantic Monthly; Chapter IV in the Saturday Evening Post; Chapter VII in the Delineator; Chapter XII in Harpers Monthly Magazine; Chapters XIII and XIV in Nature Magazine.

PREFACE

THIS volume is the first of four by Dr. William Beebe dealing with the life in the waters about Nonsuch, Bermuda. These studies are carried on by him as Director of the Department of Tropical Research of the New York Zoological Society, and financed by the generosity of Mr. Harrison Williams and the late Mortimer L. Schiff. Volumes in course of preparation are; —

MID-OCEAN:
> An account of the life of the deep sea and the author's descents in the Bathysphere.

HAND-BOOK AND KEY TO BERMUDA FISHES:
> A popular outline of the fish of this region.

LIFE HISTORIES OF BERMUDA SHORE FISH:
LIFE HISTORIES OF BERMUDA DEEP-SEA FISH:
> Elaborate monographic studies by Dr. Beebe and his staff, corresponding in scope to his Pheasant Monograph.

> MADISON GRANT
> *President,*
> New York Zoological Society

vii

ONE HUNDRED FOREWORDS

THESE chapters wrote themselves in the intervals of diving, fishing, watching, naming, dissecting, — the serious study of the fish of Bermuda. After two seasons on Nonsuch they came to mind, and, except for the first, were put down between July and October, 1931. Colors, odors, sounds and sights; the island, sea, sky and living creatures, all gloriously interexisting in the three planes of our planet, and in the fourth dimension of enthusiastic human appreciation, — all this has had to be entombed in black type upon flat paper. The chapters abound with I, Me and My, in essence the most impersonal of pronouns, standing solely for a pair of eyes, together with a moving hand whose function is that of a needle on a phonograph record, to record imperfectly what is so perfect before the directing brain begins to distort and depreciate.

CONTENTS

ILLUSTRATIONS

xiii

ILLUSTRATIONS

ILLUSTRATIONS

COURTESY NOTE

Frontispiece and Figure twenty painted by Helen Tee-Van; *Figures seven, fourteen, twenty-six and forty-three by* Else Bostelmann; *Photograph Figures one, three, eight, eighteen, twenty-four, thirty-five and forty-five by* R. Whitelaw; *Figures twenty-three and twenty-seven by* Captain Hamilton; *Figure two by* P. Dowle; *Figures twenty-five and forty-four by* J. Connery; *Figure twenty-eight by* W. Beebe; *Figures four, nine, ten, twelve, fifteen, sixteen, seventeen, nineteen, twenty-one, twenty-nine, thirty-one, thirty-two, thirty-three, thirty-eight, thirty-nine, forty, forty-one and forty-two by* A. Burg; *Figures five and six by* W. Livingston; *Figure thirty-seven by* E. R. Sanborn; *Figures eleven, thirteen, twenty-two, thirty, thirty-four and forty-six by* J. Tee-Van.

XV

NONSUCH:
Land of Water

CHAPTER I

IT was half-past four in the afternoon of the Second Day of Creation, and in a drowned world I was wet and cold and hungry and idle and bored. Then things began to happen inside my mind and at four forty-five I was still wet, but neither cold nor hungry nor idle, and hence not bored.

At the very tip of the long, southward-pointing finger of Nonsuch is a small cliff jutting out to sea between two little gorges, and on the uttermost point I was perched in a deluge of rain, hugging my knees and wishing for the sun. Only the day before I had been desirous of knowing something of the beginning of Nonsuch and of Bermuda, and now, suddenly, I realized that my wish had been answered, and instead of squatting, disgruntled and bored, I focused all my imagination on making the most of this cosmic opportunity. There must have been a moon in existence somewhere in the firmament beyond all this dampness, for the tide was high, although the horizontal water was quite hidden by the vertical downpour.

The isolation of my perch was such that not a particle of land — dry or otherwise — was visible. I would not have been surprised if a school of active

3

fish had dashed past, and twice I glanced obliquely upward, half expecting to see the keel of a boat as when I am submerged in the diving helmet. I could breathe only by keeping my head well down. Every portion of my body was wet, so having nothing for comparison, I was not conscious of moisture. At first I had been aware of dripping and splashing and the slap of waves, but these, by interminable repetition, had become part of underwater silence.

I might have been the last of the evil pre-Noahites, about to slip into oblivion. And then even this conceit left me, and I attained a damp Nirvana; hunger, cold, wetness, boredom were forgotten, and I was an utterly inadequate but appreciative mind looking on at the birth of Bermuda.

Students of the planets and of our jolly, round, whirling earth have given us an estimate of cosmic evolution considerably longer than that of the Bible. I have known days, indeed, which seemed like eternity, and Einstein tells us that space annihilates both ether and time. Still the human mind likes to mumble definite figures, even though they are far beyond actual appreciation. So I recalled with moist satisfaction that the birth of the seven seas must have been somewhere around a billion years ago. This seemed ancient even to me on my oceanic pedestal, and my mind flew ahead to the time, twenty or thirty millions of years ago, when the volcanos of the western Atlantic began to push and boil upward. Unlike the usual cluster of such outbursts, that of Burmuda was solitary in mid-ocean.

MOUNT BERMUDA

In the West Indies and Antilles, seven or eight hundred miles to the south, there were scores of neighbourly outlets which nosed their way up from the bottom into light and air, and far across the Atlantic, twenty-five hundred miles east, the volcanic constellation of the Azores broke surface.

Here in complete isolation, at the bidding of some deep-hidden geological whim, the lava began to ooze forth, and after an inconceivable chemical battle with the icy waters two miles down, piled up the scarlet, molten rock from the very vitals of Mother Earth, pitting its three thousand degrees of sheer heat against the all but freezing point of the water, backed by two tons of pressure to the inch. As far as we know today (and this knowledge barely creeps across the line from the illimitable Land of Minus) this mountain reached the surface with one peak, to a southernmost particle of which I was now clinging. But on the slopes of this great submarine massif, two mighty cones stretched themselves up — so high that they made of Bermuda almost a trio of island centers. Today they are known as the Challenger and Argus Banks, flat-topped peaks, fifteen and thirty miles off shore and only a few fathoms beneath the surface. I have dredged the former from the Arcturus and gleaned a great mass of seaweed and reef animals, and I have fished it from the Gladisfen and found it aboil with sharks. This is Bermuda mountain as we know it today.

But, to go back, here was I blinded and sur-

rounded by water, and all I knew of the world was
that I rested on a hard bit of crag — so Bermuda
must be above water. The Third Day of Genesis
was yet to dawn, for early therein is a mention of
dry land and that was, to my senses, yet to come.
Shifting my cramped limbs, I slipped and slid down
the rivulets and waterfalls until by the mere cessation of liquid sound I knew I had reached the level
of most of our globe. The downpour had long ago
flattened whatever motion the ocean might have
had of its own. I dipped still farther — the rain
ceased to pelt my knees and shoulders and I knew
I was neck deep under the sea. I reached out and
swashed the water back and forth and something
stuck between my fingers. I plucked at it and
palmed it, and climbed back upon the only material in the world which was not water. Bracing
my toes into convenient crevices I shook the water
from my eyes and gazed mistily at what I had salvaged from the waves. Vague messages traveled
from eyes to mind — strangely from a forgotten
world, a world which held such qualities as sunlight and dryness, an unwatery world. I held a
grape in my hand — that idea persisted for a long
time, and I looked steadily at it between drops, trying to picture the necessary dryness which was required to make of a grape a reality. I had almost
succeeded when a spark of accessory memory made
it plain that this could not be a grape. It might have
been several other things, but its actualness burst
upon me and for a few minutes I experienced the

joy which has come only twice before in my life;
when I have been playing a silly game with myself
and my mind (as at present hugging the idea of
the Second Day of Creation), and suddenly have
had Earth or Sky or Cosmos take a hand, lean
down, and play with me. I felt like Ord when he
glimpsed the hand of the Player enormous in the
sky, over the heads of the gods. Only in my case it
was nothing but a little green sphere, which if very
hard might have been an emerald — if sheltering a
cluster of small seeds would most assuredly have
been a grape. My second memory was correct and
I knew my fingers had closed upon a Halicystis
floating in this waste of waters. And the knowledge
that it was this, made me shout aloud into the world
of drops that the Third Day of Creation had
dawned, and I was here to see! But if I am to be a
consistent surveyor of the evolution of Nonsuch
I must keep my Halicystis shut away for a while
in my closed fist and pretend I have not yet
seen it.

Bermuda has two nicknames which to us on Nonsuch are gross misnomers. One is " The Isles of
Rest." This slogan comes stamped across our en-
velopes and for the average tourist is doubtless very
true. To us, whose work-day is measured only by
our physical being's absolute limit of energy, it is
only comic. The second is " Coral Islands," when
as a matter of fact there is not a particle of coral
in the inorganic make-up of Bermuda. Living
coral, in small and large heads, is indeed abundant

on the submerged reefs, although even here it is only a veneer of encrusted life.

Bermuda is undoubtedly the apex of a mighty volcanic mountain. A recent deep boring, made in the hope of finding fresh water, failed completely in its purpose, but provided absolute proof of ancient volcanic activity. The first three hundred and sixty feet showed limestone such as we find today everywhere in Bermuda. For the next two hundred feet yellowish clay-like rocks represented decomposed volcanic tufa. From here down to the extreme limit of boring, fourteen hundred feet, there was nothing but black volcanic rock, and this undoubtedly extended down to the very ocean floor. The only lava I have seen is a bit from the gizzard of a sandpiper, freshly arrived from Greenland. Everywhere on all the islands, are crags and cliffs and outcroppings of stratified rock, soft where newly exposed and hardened to the consistency of steel where lashed by breakers. The multitude of superimposed leaves of stone do not mark past lava flows nor deposits on an ancient sea-bottom, but sheets of wind-blown sand swirled over prehistoric dunes.

As long as my watery world reigned supreme I could well mark my data as millions upon millions of years b.c., but when the low afternoon sun began to sift through the rain, and I could dimly see the fissures and crags of the hardened wind-blown rocks of Nonsuch, then eons of time passed quickly and I again came down the scale to, geologically

8

speaking, almost contemporary times — say in early Pleistocene, about two millions of years back.

Here we have a geological conundrum: At this time, twenty thousand centuries ago, let us suppose we have a potential Bermuda submerged a little distance beneath the surface of the ocean. How can we make this into isles of rest without raising the crest of the submerged volcano or adding coral or other material to its summit? The only logical remaining possibility appears to be absurd — the lowering of the ocean itself, and yet this is exactly what happened. If a pail of water is allowed partly to freeze overnight and the ice then removed, the level of the remaining water will be considerably lowered. So, many years ago in the Pleistocene, great wind-storms carried away vast quantities of water, drawn up into clouds from the oceans, and deposited it as snow over all the northern lands of the world. The snow then turned into ice and pushed southward and the first glacial epoch began. Little by little, as more water piled up on the land, the level of the Atlantic Ocean sank, and Bermuda Mountain came nearer and nearer to the surface. Finally when over a half mile thickness of ice had formed, the level of the sea was lowered over two hundred and fifty feet, leaving Bermuda high and dry.

Dry Bermuda at this time was of considerable extent, and the terrific wind-storms probably prevented the growth of any vegetation. But snails, uncounted hosts of snails, barnacles, sea-urchins, bryozoans, and other shelly creatures found the shores excellent for existence and thrived. Generations died and their homes were smashed by the waves and ground up into sand, and this was blown into high dunes and cemented by the rain. " And so, Best Beloved," was written the second chapter of Bermuda. When I stand upon the summit of Nonsuch and look eastward toward Coopers, or south to Gurnet or west to Castle, I see everywhere the paper-thin records of past wind-borne sand (more euphoniously, aeolian), once fine as powder, now hardened into limestone or very marble. And when I dive four or five fathoms down to the bottom of Nonsuch Bay, or farther out, at Almost Island, on the edge of the ocean abyss itself, there again are everywhere the fixed records of ancient dunes.

The first time I drove across Bermuda I noticed in the sheer limestone walls where the road cut deep into the hills, an occasional stratum of rich red loam, many feet beneath the present surfaces. It remained for Dr. Sayles, when on a visit to me on Nonsuch to make plain the meaning of the several layers of earth lying between the numerous records of ancient wind-blown sand. They represent the successive interglacial periods of warmth, when the water would rise, reducing the exposed surface and curtailing the wind-blown dunes whose formation necessitated considerable areas above water. During periods such as these, the conditions would be much like the present, when the cessation of constant movement of shifting sand would permit the establishment and growth of plant life and the slow accumulation of earth and mold. In the course of time there would come another glacial period, with a re-exposing of great extents of surface, and the whirling sands would quickly destroy and bury the plants and the collected soil. And so on, until it seems certain that we can recognize no fewer than four distinct soils, representing as many inter-glacial times of windless warmth.

As the rain slackened and the afternoon sun grew stronger I saw, from my semi-aquatic seat, the grey and black crags about me. Beneath my hand was a thickened slab with six delicate layers, the fourth twice the depth of the others. I fingered this particular layer, crumbled its edge into sand grains, and flung a handful into the air. And then I tried to imagine the mighty wind which had last swirled these over the dunes and into that other air — hot or cold — which blew over this spot at least fifty thousand years before the first glimmerings of historic human life. And I and my work and my opinions seemed, like Kim, to be very small and of very little account and of no real importance what-ever. I began to muse on what was the use of it all and why bother about anything any longer, and be-cause this, like some charity, is only an inverted form of egotism and conceit, my partner in my silly game of long ago sprang another surprise. I noticed that there was a mist of sorts between me and the stratified sand near by. I looked up and as far as emotional effect went, a full charge of H E might have gone off at my elbow. I experienced a visual shell-shock, for high overhead there was etched the strongest, most materialistic rainbow I have ever seen, one end of which began in mid-air, and the other curved down, down, down, holding true from red to violet, to the rocks beside me. Once before, on a Guiana jungle river, I have been actually at the end of a rainbow, when, at my very side, one colored the bulwarks of our Akawai canoe.

As I stood up I dropped my Halicystis grape, but swiftly salvaged it again as it bobbed about on the water, not because of its rarity, but by reason of its part in my game. For on the Third Day of Creation, somewhere about seven hundred millions of years ago, when the waters and the sky and the earth had been running satisfactorily for a while, there appeared the first living organisms comparable with my pseudo-grape. For several reasons the round green Halicystis was the most appropriate of modern living beings to play the part of one of the earliest of organisms. First of all, it is a plant, an alga, and plants certainly preceded animals. And secondly, it is a single cell, and unquestionably the protophyta are the most accurately named of all groups. Again, many creatures of ancient times amaze us with their astounding size — pterodactyls, dragonflies, brontosaurs, titanotheres, moas — all exceeding any corresponding organisms living on the earth today. In Halicystis we have a contemporary miracle, no whit less wonderful than would be a living six-foot ant, or a fifty-foot dog, or a hundred-foot man. When we think of a single cell we think automatically of something microscopic, such as the cells in the human body which have a maximum diameter of a fraction of a millimeter. In Halicystis, however, we have a large green marble, probably the largest cell in the world.

Aside from its interest, so germane to my present mood, Halicystis is a very remarkable organism. The Bermudians call them sea-bottles, and after storms they are sometimes found in dozens washed ashore along the south beach on Nonsuch. They have great resiliency, and when fresh and alive will bounce five or six feet from a smooth surface. When the sun shines brightly upon a group on the sand just as they have been left by the waves, their beauty is that of polished emeralds — the sunlight passing through their translucent green substance and deeply staining their thin shadow.

They may be round or pyriform and no one knows where they begin life, whether hidden beneath some rock near shore, or as is more probable, farther out in the mysterious mid-zone. Unlike related forms, when freed from their slight attachment they float buoyantly. In an aquarium they will live for a week or more and then gradually pale out until they are like ghosts of grapes, and little by little, settle to the bottom with only a few jade-colored granules in place of the nucleus and all the complex vital mechanism of this " simple " plant of the sea. I have measured a Halicystis one and one-half inches in diameter and they have been reported to grow as large as a hen's egg. The ease of collection of this and related sea-bottles and the extraordinary size of these single cells, has led to the detailed study of the effects of electricity and various chemical compounds and elements upon them — experimentation which may conceivably lead to better knowledge of cellular health and disease in the human body.

And now for two exciting sequences: I published this chapter in the *Atlantic Monthly,* and at once had a telephone from a Great Physicist, who is also to me a Best Friend.

" Ho! Ho! " said he, " at last I have caught you in an honest error. I believe you thought you saw, but you could not possibly have seen, a rainbow which began at your very side, and yet which arched away into a curve overhead. Optics say impossible. I will tell you about it when I see you."

A week later the G. P. who was also the B. F. lunched with me, and when pencils gave out, we used forks on the tablecloth, much to the waiter's anguish and my confusion, for by this time the G. P. had worked himself into a fever heat of joy, because he had discovered that I probably did see what I wrote, explicable only by a little known kink of physics, a kink whose mathematical formulas left me hopelessly stranded. It will be published in some suitable place, and I shall then point with pride to the proof of my experience, but in this world I shall never exactly understand it.

MOUNT BERMUDA

As to the geology of Bermuda, I combined all the observations I could make, and then picked the brains of the best geologists I knew, and patting the islands on the back said to myself, " And so, that is how you came to be Bermuda."

In the course of my more serious researches, to which these essays may be said to be only an authentic fringe, I made a series of dredge hauls on the bottom of my deep-sea study area. One memorable day, my sturdy little cob-web of wire brought the big dredge to the surface twelve miles off shore. Soundings had shown that the bottom here was fifteen hundred fathoms or a full mile and a half beneath our keel. The dredge frame was twisted and bent into a V by the roughness over which it had passed, which was in itself surprising, for at such a depth the bottom of the ocean, even if rolling, is usually smooth.

The netting itself was not torn, and although there were only a few handfuls of abyssal loot at the end, these were most amazing. They consisted wholly of water-worn shells, bits of coral and rounded pebbles — indisputable proofs of a submerged beach. There was half a hundred of one species of white bivalve which has been found fossil in Bermuda cliffs thirty feet above the present ocean level and most of the shells are of West Indian species.

So here is an entirely new glimpse of the past of Bermuda. The glacial earths and wind-blown sand are unquestionably facts. But ages and ages before the terrestrial tides of ice ebbed and flowed, the bottom of the sea hereabouts would seem by some unprecedented extent of upheaval, to have been dry land.

At present Bermuda has nearly the same area as Manhattan Island — about twenty square miles; when the ocean was partly evaporated into ice it multiplied this nearly twelve times, while a conservative estimate of dry land, if my mile and a half deep beaches cannot be otherwise explained, would give to Bermuda an area of almost six hundred square miles.

There seems no possible chance of the shells and pebbles having rolled or fallen to these great depths down such a gentle slope, and the fact of their being the same as those from the West Indies gives the whole matter great significance.

In spite of all these new and exciting discoveries, I still get sheer joy out of my first game. And to-day when I walk on Nonsuch Beach, with the storm's aftermath pounding on the sand, the small, stranded green globes appeal to me not only with their intrinsic beauty, but they recall the delight that one of them gave, when it so fittingly ushered into my imagination the dawn of the Third Day of Creation — a matter of more than half a billion years gone by.

1. Millions of years ago Mount Bermuda nosed its way to the upper air through two miles of ocean.

2. Modern Mount Bermuda from the air.

CHAPTER II

THE CEDARS OF NONSUCH

EVERY time I come up from diving among the coral reefs I find I have an increased interest in botany. Under water I associate with an astonishing number of animals masquerading as plants; sea-lilies, lichens, fungus, moss, grass, fruit, trees, vines, blossoms, shrubs, ancient and weather-beaten trees — all are represented, and only by careful scrutiny is the animal character apparent. I come up and see the trees and lesser plants of Nonsuch swaying in the currents of air. I note their forms, colors, and patterns, and instinctively I watch for sudden unplantish movements. I look for a visiting insect to be seized and eaten; I wonder if the jellyfish which drops when ripe from the branch of his parent has no simile on land.

And then I think of the sundew trapping and devouring its prey, of the nervousness of sensitive plants, of the capable defense of nettles, of the sleeping postures of flowers, and the almost reasoned efforts of vines to attain light and water. There come to mind the terrible tragedies of trees choked to death by parasites; the time when a bamboo sprout carried my hat out of reach in three days, and the sad death of a carrot from alcoholism

17

as portrayed by Sir Chandra Bose. The sleep of plants must be a very light one, and stirred by many ambitious dreams.

The plants of Nonsuch Island have a compelling interest wholly lacking in those of a great tropical forest or in Canadian woods. An army, as an abstract thing, has no vital, absorbing interest, but a single soldier may hold our attention unwaveringly. In a jungle our concentration is distracted by the multiplicity of forms which cover every inch of ground and reach high up into the sky. On Nonsuch I could easily count the cedar trees and learn something of the individuality of each.

One trenchant difference between the pseudo-flora of undersea and land vegetation is that the currents seem to have no effect on the shape of the former. Branch coral, in fact, seems to lean a little toward any steady current of water, perhaps because it carries the only source of food. Sea-plumes are eager, as children at table are eager — swaying slightly toward the door of the butler's pantry whence dessert is imminent. I am certain that no bend of abyssal branch or twist of animal blossom anywhere reveals the direction of the Gulf Stream.

Whether on one of those rare Bermuda days when not a breath stirs and the sea is glassy, or when a northeast storm is raging, a single glance at the cedars before my laboratory, and I could predict southerly and westerly winds for well-nigh the remaining three hundred and sixty-three days of the year!

THE CEDARS OF NONSUCH

The moulding power of the invisible is a theme which in force and effect is worthy of the best expression that human mind can give, and the thoughts I have about my leaning cedars are very wonderful ones. They stir and rise in my mind, they course down my arm and hand, reach my penpoint, and — dry there.

Nonsuch botany spreads over half the world, not only as immigrants and stowaways, but in the power of suggestion. Witness the cedars. I listen at night to the wind soughing through their branches, I sniff at a bunch of the dried, leafy twigs hung over my bed, and as the dawn comes up and snuffs out many stars, a planet or two, and St. David's light, the tossing of dark green foliage outside my door is the undulating of a magic emerald carpet, which, aided by the sound and scent, carries me mentally, sensually, and emotionally to the biting cold among the deodars of Garhwal.

A hundred feet from my doorway is a solid clump of cactus. I have not yet tried this, but I am sure that one day I shall sit down close to it in a driving rain, with the surf pounding full-voiced a few yards beyond and hurling spray over me with every breaker. And I am equally certain that contemplation of the strange, thorny pads will be all that will be necessary to obliterate sight, sound, and feel of a Bermuda gale, and substitute the hot, dry breathlessness of a sandy desert. The mere mention of the illusion at this moment is fostered by the caroling of a Japanese robin in the distance, which recalls,

19

for me, the first unbelievable notes of a canyon wren in a Mexican arroyo.

One memorable evening on Nonsuch my path was suddenly blocked by an odor — so abrupt, so intense, that it might well have been a tangible barrier, and out of the exhalation of a new-born cereus were conjured all the subconsciously recorded details of a Guiana jungle. Leaving all abstract sentiment, I sit down anywhere among the open vegetation of Nonsuch and am at home — head deep in a field of goldenrod.

I cannot keep away from the theme of the cedars, for their importance is dominant. Even Dr. Britton writes of the Bermuda juniper as " one of the most interesting of all trees," and if " N. L." himself thinks so, after his intimacy with alphas and omegas of plants, there is no doubt about it. If Bermuda were decedared it would enter the category of desert islands. Brangman, near us, is epitomized by the fact that not even a cedar grows upon it. In a land of immigrants, stowaways, and garden escapes, the cedar can boast of autochthonous origin, which is a hot-potato-mouth way of saying it is an original inhabitant.

The first arrivals, who were also the first humans to be washed ashore from the outer reefs, found forests of cedars. From these the survivors of the wrecks of the Bonaventura and the Sea Venture were able to build ships strong enough to carry them to Newfoundland and to Virginia. Later settlers had excellent reasons for denuding the island of these primitive giants, for at that time they had not learned the Bermuda method of building comfortable, everlasting houses by sawing out a cellar and piling it up. The intimate place of the cedar in human life is indicated by the perfect suitability of the fragrant, wine-colored wood for the fashioning of cradles, wedding-chests and coffins, to say nothing of ducking stools and gallows. As early as 1622 a law was passed to prevent complete deforestation; today one cherishes these trees like precious tapestries or netsukes.

There is no question of the native character of the Bermuda cedar; it is found growing wild nowhere else in the world. But a delicate question of its scientific name gives to think of the exciting laws of scientific nomenclature. One hundred and sixty years after Henry May of the Bonaventura was saved by a cedar " barke " which he and his shipmates built in Bermuda, Linnaeus figured two cedars on the same page, the first of which he called *Juniperus barbadensis* and the second *bermudiana,* for self-evident reasons. There is cause now to think that both were specimens of the Bermuda cedar, in which case the good and true meaning of language must be sacrificed to give place to priority, which is the handmaiden of Einstein's place-time. Yet, though we laugh at calling the Bermuda cedar *barbadensis,* there is a sound basic idea in it — the necessity of uniformity in humanistic views of science.

But let us go a little way beyond Linnaeus, beyond Henry May, before the ancestors of Bermudez ever were, and before the time of the first Bermuda cedar tree. Today we know that the nearest related cedar is that of Cuba — nine hundred miles to the southeast. Day after day in April and May I watch newly arrived birds on Nonsuch which have made this distance in one flight. I put several cedar berries into our bird cage and they are snapped up at once. The following morning the hard seeds lie on the earth of the cage, stripped clean of flesh and ready for sprouting. The application of these various facts is only an extension of the fence lines of young cedars in upland New England pastures, unconsciously planted and aligned by roosting wax-wings. And so, we have the probable story of how the juniper came to Bermuda.

On the north or sheltered slopes of Nonsuch the cedars grow high and symmetrically. They stretch their branches lazily up and outward, and their trunks have thickened steadily and grown straight through the years. The sound of the surf comes faintly from the distance and now and then the howl of gales passes just overhead in company with low, scudding storm clouds. But these proud young cedars have no fear of the elements. There is hardly a dead branch among them, and, like the winter coat of camels, their outside bark hangs loose and dangles undisturbed. We pass over the crest of the island and come to my particular trees, just in front of my door. They still have plenty of height and girth; I can easily walk about beneath their branches, but their tops are flattened out and they lean rather heavily to the north and east. Beyond them, farther down the slope, the cedars begin to crouch with humped shoulders, their backs turned toward the blasts, their fingers stretched ahead, dodging one another for light and air, but with stream lines lying in the paths of least resistance. And now we approach the very edge of the low ledge on whose farther side lies death to all beings of land. Yet the phalanx of brave cedars does not falter. All soil has gone, there are only rugged rocks with cracks and crevices for foothold. The branches sweep the ground, bracing themselves here and there with knotty elbows. In size, trunks have become branches, branches twigs, yet all keep their character. Given the slightest shelter of a hollow and a cedar staggers to its knees, a replica of the pines of Fujiyama.

These cedars on their knees are the most interesting of all. They emerge from their natal crack in a great gnarly mass of indeterminate root-stem. Their trunk is in appearance a horizontal branch, conforming to the angle of the hill, yet clear of it. I rather imagine that the terrific rasping of merely resting upon the rocks would spell destruction within a few gales' time. It would seem as if the eternal blasting power of the wind fairly blows the sap of life out of the windward branches, for most of these are dead, with occasional spurts of green springing from the heart of the straggling, bleached, branch bones, the skeleton of long-past years. Some-

23

times perhaps the killing was quickly done — some devastating storm of many days' duration which kept air and twigs saturated with salt.

Beyond the asylum of the shell-hole hollows, down go the cedars on all fours again. Now the sea-lavender and the ox-eye and even the lowly tassel-plant call them brother; a little farther waterward and the arboreal dwarfs mingle with the prostrate stems of the seaside morning-glories, creeping upon their bellies, but still with every proud character of their race, their leaf-strung twigs no whit different from those waving fifty feet above ground.

I like to go down to this front line of battle in a high wind and see the opposing forces in full action. Surely it must have been during a lull that a berry rolled or was carried into this far crevice. It sprouted and took root, and soon the first test came. Since then the pressure has been almost mathematically constant, for the plant to adjust root and height so nicely to maintain its balance and hold. One day last week, from no especial stress of weather, one of the proud cedars of the north slope fell over, perhaps from its overconfident topheaviness. Its roots sprawled in mid-air, rather soft and of no great length. Here, where seventh waves spout spray over me as I sit, I use all my strength, and pluck a cedarling from its crack. It is not a foot high and has twenty slender, leaf-scaled twigs. Its root is three times as thick as its superstructure, twice as long, and has five lateral rootlets, revealing as many side cracks. I go a few yards inland, and replant the sturdy little cedar, giving it a most excellent crack and mulched, tamped-down earth. Then, wholly without justice or logic, I pull up one of its brethren of similar size and cut through the rooty stem, to find that it started life about nine years ago.

In a little depression, in the sheltered lee of a giant brother, an infant cedar sprouted less than a year ago. There is none of the blue-green, close-scaled character of the older plants, but widespread, pale emerald, spinelike leaves, which show more in common with the creeping spurge on the rock beneath. Like the cedars of the northern slopes, the infant thinks the whole world is an easy place to live in, and is only lulled by the roar of the storms. Doubtless it looks with scorn at its brethren overhead, bowing before the blasts. But when its pliant topmost twig reaches the level of the surrounding rocks, and a winter's gale flattens it like tissue, the roots will have to develop new strength and the fancied security of the little plant must give place to the glory of lifelong combat. After long search I find the whole story on one small plant — smug, juvenile confidence, adolescent surprise and quick preparedness, and finally the dense, close-scaled armor and adequate defense of maturity. For every cedar which has fought its way to success, thousands upon thousands must have sprouted, lived hopefully for a space, only to have their sap die down and cease, lifelessly to hold aloft futile, dead twigs, until at last these fell and returned to the stuff of which cedars are made.

The berries on my laboratory trees are now, in August, ready to fall, much eaten by insects and long past their prime. Beyond, in Sprayland, close to the ocean, the crop of cedar berries has only begun; they are either very small, just after flowering, or still greenish white with none of the purplish bloom of maturity. And the male trees are still powdered with the last billion grains of pollen dust. The tiny feminine cedars seem to win in the last test; at the sheer rim of the ocean I find a pitiful offering of berries, perhaps four on the whole plant, fertilized in the very mist from the breakers, and maturing where they are reflected in the tidepools. These heroic bitter-enders can scatter their offspring nowhere but in the ocean itself — achieving victory under terrific obstacles, for a culmination only of defeat.

I climb back to the second line, where the kneeling cedars draw breath between storms. Prying up the stiff branches and scraping away some of the sandstone, I find ancient trunks sprouting from still older bases. One of these is a bole of unusually large size, one end of which was in some long-past year cut off rather unskillfully with an axe. I bare part of the circumference, the rest being hidden behind recently solidified sand. A fourteen-inch cedar on the north slope of Nonsuch had seventy-nine rings. This old, bleached, metal-hard trunk shows one hundred far from the heart.

THE CEDARS OF NONSUCH

My final count of two hundred and seventy-six is conservative, for I could not reach the very center, nor was the chopping an event of the immediate past. I scratched on a smooth bit of sandstone the sum in subtraction, and got my initial date as 1653. In an attempt to cut off a splinter, my knife blade broke as cleanly as if I had tried to whittle a steel girder.

I looked over to Castle Island and realized that its old, ruined fort had been built forty years before my tree had taken root. But not until I returned to the laboratory and delved into Bermudian history could I fix on any single item of this year. In an old archive I found that in St. Georges, three miles away to the northeast, on April 17, 1653, there took place the trial of John Middleton for witchcraft. The evidence of one Robert Priestly was as follows:

" Who saith that on Fryday last, being the 15th of this instant, he being removeing Mr. Tucker's cattell in the evening in a piece of ground near to the house of John Middleton, he saw right oppositt agt the house, a Black creatuer lye soe upon the ground in the shape of a catt but farre Bigger, with eyes like fier, and a tayle near as long as a mans arme. And this examynate being some whitt daunted at the first sight, yet tooke courage & went upp close to yt to look on yt. he only saw it move the head, and drawne his knife with a resolution to stabb yt: as he lift up his hand and knife to strike at yt with all his force, he being a strong man, he

27

found he had no power to strike it. Att which this examanate was so amazed and affrighted that his hayre stood up right on his head, and he departening from yt looked backe, & sawe the said creatuer turn the heade and look wishfully after this examt, but he ran away & left yt: reporting the same to the servant in his house, with much feare. And further saith not."

After prolonged evidence and examination, the account of the trial concludes:

" The Jury for the keeper of the Commonwealth of England doth present John Middleton of Sandys Tribe in the Somer Islands, Planter, for that he not having the feare of God before his eyes hath feloniously wickedly and abominably consulted and consented to and with the Devil to become a witch. As doth appear by severall signes and markes upon his body, and that diabolicall sin of witch-craft hath put in practice now lately upon the Body or person of John Makaraton, a skotsman of about the age of 50 years: and him hath vexed and tormented and disquieted contrary to the peace of the Commonwealth of England and the dignity thereof.

" This Bill being put to the consideration of the Grand Inquest was found *Billa vera* and for his further triall he put himselfe upon God and Country, whereof a jury of 12 men sworne did find him guilty, and sentence of death was pronounced upon him, and he wase executed at Georges towne at the common place of execution the 9th day of May 1653."

THE CEDARS OF NONSUCH

Brother Middleton, when he saw there was no escape for himself, apparently decided to make it unpleasant for sundry persons for whom he did not care. For example, he testified against one Goody Christian Stevenson, who, although a kindly soul, always helping her neighbors in times of sickness and trouble, yet, because two small warts inside her mouth did not bleed when pricked, was convicted and hung eleven days after John Middleton.

So it was with such things as these that my cedar in early life was contemporary. And I marveled. Then I looked toward the northeast, my mind going many miles beyond St. Georges to the land of America and to Tennessee; I remembered the arguments against the teaching of Evolution, and it occurred to me that this was only some five years ago — and I marveled again!

If the plants of Nonsuch could, like the morning stars, sing together, the chorus of Cedar and Sage and Goldenrod would arise from nine-tenths of them, these three natives forming the major part of the trees, the shrubs and the weed-like annuals. Yet there are dozens of others all represented by a few plants. As I look over a list which we made out in early spring, I am impressed with the charm of the common names, something almost wholly lacking in fish. When we return from a fishing trip we have hamlets, hinds, gags, groupers, porgies, and breams — titles as uncouth and meaningless as their owners are graceful and beautiful. But sea-lavender, seaside goldenrod, tassel-plant, sea rocket, star-of-the-earth, mallow, rosy primrose, oleander, poor-man's-weatherglass, match-me-if-you-can, — these are a delight to tell over, euphonious or meaningful, or both.

In spring, Nonsuch is ablaze with thousands of pink stars as the oleanders burst forth; later comes the rose red of hibiscus, and gradually, in the autumn months, a background of golden spires sets the island again on fire. It is a pleasant alarm when a half-grown great blue heron rises with a sudden raucous outburst from the beach, or a young tropic-bird squawks beneath your very feet, but to be surprised by a flower is an even keener joy. I recall a waste of grey and silver rocks, from which a tiny brilliant face looked up at me, and I saw my first scarlet pimpernel. And after I had found others and had become used to them, I stumbled unexpectedly upon the rare blue race, and Nonsuch gained a new charm. Nothing becomes more monotonous, mile after mile through a car window, than endless wheat fields, and yet to us the finding of a single stalk of wheat growing on our island was a memorable event. It was very probably the only living wheat for a thousand miles. In the matter of plant surprises we need not wallow forever in sweet sentimentalism — the careless somnambulist on Nonsuch may encounter cactus or nettle, obliterating for the time being all charm of botany.

I have made a list of the plants of Nonsuch according to distribution and probable method of arrival. The European and West Indian derivations are about equal, and from the latter region about as many must have reached Bermuda by floating as were carried by birds, while a much smaller number doubtless braved the hundreds of miles of water by parachuting on the steady southeast winds.

An illustration of the distributing powers of winged seeds came to notice close to my laboratory. A dense growth of green weeds sprang up early in the year on the site of an old garden, and in July blossomed and formed seed. It proved to be the hairy horseweed, and from this time on we seldom forgot the hairy horseweed, alias *Leptilon linifolium.* In coffee cups, aquaria, in deep-sea hauls from a mile down, between one's eyes and book, entangled in pen points — everywhere the tiny, pappus-winged seeds drifted their way, soundless and buoyant as diminutive balloons.

One of my last walks was through the cedar forest of the sheltered slope. The pounding of the surf was inaudible here, but a low restless wind eddied down through the branches. I stood and listened, and heard a perfect reproduction of the sound of the waves as I should hear them beyond the crest. It was most strange to listen to this false echo among the trees, a sound as hollow and meaningless to these pampered cedars as the roaring of the ocean which we like to fancy lies in a seashell.

When I come to choose a plant to carry back to my home, I shall creep far into one of the great caves which wind and water have etched into the heart of Nonsuch, and beneath a sunlit crevice I shall pick a root of maiden-hair fern — one whose ancestor was carried (who knows how many years this side of the last glacial epoch) high in air, the atoms of spores whirling as they swept onward, billions of them dusting the troubled waters of mid-ocean, until this one alighted in safety. And it must have alighted not only on land, but on some particular bit of soil suitable for germination and fruition. When next we are carried away with enthusiasm by some new feat of airplanes, let us not forget the Flight of the First Fern.

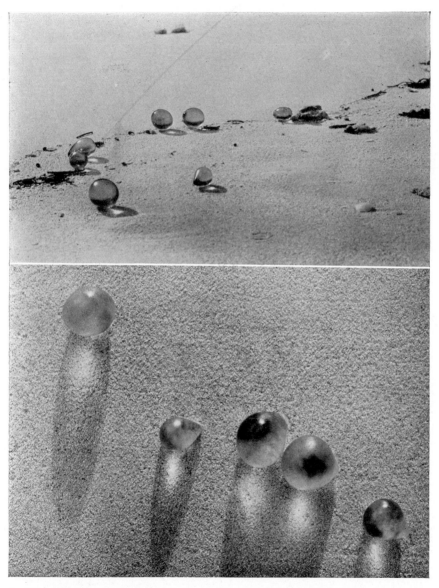

3. The largest single cells in the world: *Halicystis*, a one-celled seaweed, known in Bermuda as sea bottles, and looking like emeralds.

4. The water-worn gorges show the many lines of wind-blown eolian sand.

CHAPTER III

SIX years ago I drifted in the Arcturus for ten days in the Pacific, hovering above a certain spot in mid-ocean and by dredge, net and sounding wire learning everything I could about this invisible but very real bit of submerged earth.

Six days ago I made my first map of Almost Island, south of Nonsuch, and northeast of Gurnets Rock. We are accustomed to speak of air pockets and mountain chains and hanging valleys, so why cannot we have something which is almost an island? The distinction is much more accurate than that between hill and mountain, creek and river. I might in fact call my area Once Island for from its configuration and our knowledge of the land hereabouts, there is no doubt that it was formerly well above water.

I discovered it by accident three years ago when I rowed out to Gurnets, threw out the anchor at random and went down in the helmet. I found myself in five or six fathoms on the whitest of sand, looking up at the walls of a splendid reef — great cliffs waving with sea-fans and alive with fish. The minute the helmet was removed I located the spot definitely in its relation to Gurnets Rock

— two hundred yards southwest of my boat and marked by a giant angle in the center of the reef.

Almost Island is in an exposed position, separated from the open sea by only a few yards of reefs and boilers. Swells coming in do not actually break, but they swirl around the boilers and begin to slow up and gain height at the friction of the shallows. My first problem was to arrange for a safe landing whenever the wind and sea permitted. We tried throwing out an anchor to windward, with the result that we usually lost the anchor or had a difficult time freeing it, and often the stern of the launch would swing in a quarter circle, chafing the metal ladder against the reef. A heavy piece of iron and a chain, attached to a log buoy well to windward helped, and finally another far out on the sand made my island easy of access; the boat was like a double-moored zeppelin over an inaccessible island above water.

Proper islands are delineated by geographers and the makers of maps with rulers and compasses, squares and dividers. I was my own dividers in the present instance.

While my bit of land more than justified the name of island by being surrounded with water, yet its actual area was extremely personal and ungeographic. I estimate it to be roughly circular and about one hundred and fifty feet in diameter. As I say I was the measuring dividers — the pump on the launch being the center, the hose the radial string and I the pen or pencil or marker on the periphery.

My apparatus is, of course, our old story — the same double-action pump, a forty-foot metal ladder, two generous lengths of hose and the metal helmet with four weights, which I have used for years in the Galápagos and West Indies. The helmets are dull now and show hard usage, dents from over-hanging Galápagos lava blocks, scratches from the low-arched tunnels of Cocos and Panama, and the branching coral in Haiti. But they are as good as ever, fitting to the back and shoulder like well-worn clothing.

The helmet on, I straightened out and slid down the ladder, reaching out my hand now and then to orient myself. Two swallows en route are usually sufficient to equalize the air pressure in my ears. I touched bottom gently, settled my helmet and looked up. This is probably the most instinctive movement of anyone, beginners or old veteran divers — a desire to make certain that the only line of retreat is open. Daily overhead I saw the amusing keel of the launch, rolling slowly in the swell — the fore and aft ropes looping into blue distance, the long sinuous black snake of a hose, with my head in its maw and its tail vanishing above the keel. The ladder waved slowly back and forth, from the sand beneath my feet up to heaven, and while I was not privileged to see angels ascending and descending, I did rejoice in the sight of jolly sergeant majors, or abudefdufs as I prefer to call them, with black stripes over green and gold, weaving in and out in my wake. They had already scented the bit of high bait I was carrying and to them I was only the harmless conveyor of something exciting and edible. A last glance up showed two things — first, a rather nice submarine joke, for close on the tail of the last abudefduf hastened a young angelfish and I chuckled and felt that Jacob in his vision had nothing on the realities of Almost Island. Second, I saw a square window opening into my other world — my assistant peering down through the water-glass. I waved and then, the whole upper seascape was obliterated by a rush of my breath bubbles and I turned to the affairs of the island.

My island is divided almost equally into sand and reef, and these correspond to all the varied phases of dry physical geography — sand taking the place of deserts, plains, pampas and tundras, and a reef embodying mountains, canyons and jungles.

We do not think of there being weather under water, but if we consider terrestrial weather as heat, cold, dryness, moisture, wind, rain, snow and fog, then my submerged islet has weather in abundance. I may descend in water which feels delightfully warm to my skin but in half an hour I come shivering to the surface with teeth chattering; as to dryness we submariners know nothing, except concerning our face, and when dryness leaves the helmet, we expire or ascend; of moisture we have nothing else but.

Wind and fog are interesting; the latter on land is

Photograph by William Livingston.

5. A sixty-foot cliff showing the alternate soil and sand
layers of three glacial periods.

Photograph by William Livingston.

6. Palmetto palms buried in a sand-storm at least two hundred
thousand years ago.

caused by minute particles of water; while beneath the surface fog is a result of small particles of land. I have visited my island when I could not see more than a yard away — the water was merely diluted sand. A distant gale had sent in great swells which reached down, down, and ploughed the sand into deep transverse furrows, while the suspended grains flicked against the glass of my helmet like atoms made visible. To see the reef or a great fish loom up through this pale-blue fog is a sight to be forever remembered. In a heavy swell the water is often filled with fronds and strands of seaweed, torn off by the surge near the surface, and now, like beautiful autumn leaves, eddying back and forth — bits of wine-colored lace, or long fronds shimmering in the diluted sunlight with exquisite opalescence.

Under-sea wind is once removed from wind overhead, since it is the motion of water caused in turn by the motion of air. I never realized how absolutely still water could be until I looked out from my Bathysphere into the blue quiet a quarter mile down. In that place there was no such thing actually as plankton, for no matter how slight a power of movement any creature might have, yet even if it shot about only in circles, the movement and direction were its own.

On my island in a heavy wind-swell, all of us, the fish and myself, became very nearly plankton, being pushed forward and withdrawn at the will of the water. Six fathoms down day and night are unlike those on land — the former being much shorter. My island is in full illumination from ten to three o'clock, preceded and followed by a prolonged dawn and dusk. It is as though the eternal night of all except the surface film of ocean was reluctant to admit any light. But my eyes become dusk-adapted very soon and even in cloudy weather I can watch my tenants, little and big.

The reef-cliffs are sandstone, etched and worn into arches, turrets, alleys, tunnels, wells, canyons and a thousand unnamable forms, by the wind and rain of some past glacial age when all were high and dry. This is overlaid and frescoed with great balls of brain coral, and hung and planted with rainbow-tinted seaweed and purple and brown sea-fans and plumes. In and out of the tangled scenery swim hosts of fish, great parti-colored parrots, surgeons of heavenly blue, angelfish, groupers, rockfish, snappers, agile wrasse of a hundred colors, and small folk by the dozen.

But this is not an ichthyological reconnaissance, it is a visit to Almost Island. Access made easy, what can I do? First and last in importance in our work is concentrated observation — remembered facts of color, movement, feeding, sociability, courtship, abundance; but I wish also to collect any new species I see, or any which defy indentification on the fin.

First comes the small trident with a three-foot metal handle. This requires the most careful stalking and yields poorest results, yet I have again and again caught a desired fish close to the reef-wall on the sand, and by a very sudden and forceful thrust

have impaled my game. I have now, however, rele-
gated Neptune's weapon, together with air rifles,
to the island armory of relics. The most efficient arm
is a wire arrow projected through a short bit of pipe
by means of a large rubber band — a cross between
a sling-shot and a bow and arrow.

My last foray will serve as a type of submarine
collecting. I dropped to the bottom with my arrow-
sling in my hand and leaning down picked up the
trident. There was only a gentle surge, what we
might call a water-breeze, and I leaned against it
and pushed south to my favorite angle. With one
hand I lifted myself three feet, found a hollow for
my foot and looked around. A short distance ahead
was a huge spined urchin, hundreds of its twelve-
inch black needles forming an impenetrable
chevaux-de-frise. With the trident I jabbed lustily
into this mass, threw the instrument behind me on
the sand and stepped down again.

Now I performed an acrobatic feat which would
win fame and fortune in vaudeville. I waited until
the surge was half through the backward push and
leaped upward with all my might. Slowly I rose and
rose off the sand, higher and higher, being carried
all the time slightly back and away from the reef.
At my greatest elevation, the surge shifted, hung
on dead center a moment, and then carried me forward and over the edge of the wall of coral and sea-
plumes. My gentle descent had already begun so
that at the end of the trajectory I found myself
close to the place from which I had chosen to op-

erate. Keeping an upright balance was the only thing to be careful about en route, but at the minute of landing it was necessary to dig in at once. With all my fingers, and my feet in their mobile, rubber-soled sneakers, I grasped every projection possible. In this case I found I could even jam an angle of the helmet against an overhanging corner. All this was to prevent my being swept off the reef by the retreating surge, and to guard against scraping in the opposite direction on razor-sharp corals and still more unpleasant spiny urchins. The one I had stabbed was close by, and the stream of luscious odor-taste pouring forth had already proved a magnet to a school of sergeant majors. Fish are like vultures and when they see an excited mob of abu-defdufs milling around a certain spot, no hint of odor or taste is needed to urge them to hurry to the place. The sequence is much the same as a light in the water at night, or a great jungle tree felled in the tropics — first come the smaller creatures, then the larger, and finally the great carnivores who are attracted not by the lure of bait, or light, or bark, but by the chance of feeding on the mob itself.

I sat with rubber sling drawn taut, feet braced against the surge, but body and head giving as much as possible to it. Here is a real under-sea rhythm, not found anywhere else, to which every fish and floating form of life, every loose strand of weed or plume, all with one impulse, swing slowly first in one direction, then all back again. I aimed at fish after fish, and then an unusually colored

40

rock-fish drifted out from between my legs and I let go. He was larger and stronger than I thought and with a half dozen tremendous flicks he tore loose. Instead of fleeing, he turned and snapped at the arrow point which still held several scales.

Smaller fish were easy to hold when once the arrow was well through, and the astonishing thing was that after being shaken off into a pail they recovered, and later in an aquarium swam upright and healed quickly. When an arrow merely grazed the side of a fish, it invariably turned and bit at the weapon and then swam off and rubbed its scaleless patch against coral and reef. A badly wounded fish which escaped, illustrated one of the fundamental laws of this underworld — one which holds in all the places and oceans where I have dived. An uninjured fish is comparatively safe, but an injured one is attacked and killed by every carnivorous fish in sight, including the members of its own school. Even the parrots and the surgeons mill excitedly about and seem to deplore the fact that they are vegetarians and can take no part in this summary execution. To us it seems cruel, or a better term perhaps is inhuman, in the real meaning of the word. If our far distant ancestors had not kept the race fit in some such way, perhaps we would not today have the stamina to carry on and yet cherish our weaklings and cripples, wage war with poison gas instead of clubs and too often forget the sheer joy of hard creative work.

NONSUCH

The most successful method of individual collecting on Almost Island is with a fish pole and a dynamite cap at the end. " Fisherman's luck " is a truism where traps, nets and angling are concerned, but this underwater shooting which I have invented elevates the collecting of fish into the realm of true sport.

On one of my last descents I located two schools of young fish. I had a hand net, but I might as well have tried to capture a pheasant on the wing with a butterfly net. The net swung so slowly through this dense medium that the youngsters did not even hurry, they simply slipped to one side into safety.

I ascended swiftly, asked for the dynamite cap, and descended. Sand once more underfoot I saw the fish pole standing upright beside me. With my net in my belt, the pole in my right hand, the insulated electric wire in the other, I was ready for action. I drifted slowly toward the smaller school of iridescent fish, stretched out my pole into their midst as far as I could, turned my head and pulled thrice on a small rubber cable. Instantly my ears were deafened and my body and limbs tingled as from a wholesale electric shock. I invariably felt of the edges of the glass after an explosion to see if all was right. Formerly I used to rest the apparatus on a bit of projecting reef and placing some bait near the cap, fire it from a distance. Now I do not mind holding the end of the five-foot pole, but as yet I have not been able to summon sufficient courage to face the explosion.

ALMOST ISLAND

I dropped the pole and it was drawn swiftly up, then I began to weave the net back and forth in the water, scooping in the floating silvery motes. I dared not stop the movement or the net would turn inside out. I found small fish of other species drifting a little distance away, but I had to work fast, for the fish were usually only stunned and soon began to recover. In such fashion I gathered fifty-odd and on deck we found they were beautiful little pear-shaped infants, all shining gold and silver with enormous gleaming eyes, blessed with the title of *Pempheris,* but no popular name.

A more exciting use of the dynamite cap was in shooting larger fish, and this hunting demanded every bit of my skill; the search for and the discovery of some desired species, the cunning stalk over sand and reef, both hunter and game at the mercy of the swell, and finally the advance of the little red lozenge, the signal, the invariable flinching and the instant pursuit and capture of the up-turned fish, to forestall any of its fellows who would at once rush in to the attack. With this sport and that of shooting flyingfish from the bow of a launch, no game-bird hunter away from his coverts or preserves or jungles need be bored.

At first sight the sand appeared barren as a desert, but I spent many dives sitting or lying as flat as my helmet would permit, watching the tenants of the shifting grains. At certain angles and strength of current and tide, the very furrows seem to be alive — having movement and rhythm, and

43

I am sure if I had a microphone I could hear the sand grains singing together.

I once sat far out on the flat, white expanse when the water was quite clear. I could feel the very slight push and slack of the swell, but the surface of the sand was troubled with a wholly different force. When my whole being was impelled forward, the crests of the furrows beyond me loosened, thousands of glittering motes rose a little, then tumbled down the slope and up the flank of the succeeding furrow. I stopped calling them furrows and recognized them as new and strange waves, tuned, like my own actions, into slow-motion imitations of our corresponding activities in another world. I saw that the sand waves were not stationary but were very slowly advancing. In five minutes my foot was well covered, and I visualized slow entombment if I stayed long enough, the creeping up and burying by the white arenaceous coverlet, — and I knew how fossils must have felt in the making.

It is not easy to see and study the creatures of the sand from a six-foot distance. One must kneel or sit, Again and again a sliver of sand slips from beneath my hand, and a sand goby has shifted its position; or as I walk along, an active snowshoe dodges my step, and a great flounder undulates to safety. The thought of gobies gives me a conceit of sorts, for here in six fathoms I found sand gobies and reef gobies but never tidepool gobies, and I realized that I — a mere land-bound human — had descended well below the realm of these shore fish. I

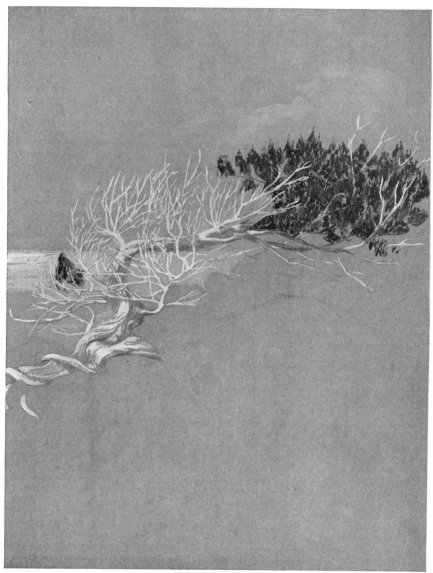

Painting by Else Bostelmann.

7. A stunted cedar of Nonsuch, two hundred and seventy-six years old.

8. Nonsuch vegetation: Cedar trees and undergrowth of goldenrod and sagebush.

once went to the trouble of carrying down a shore goby in a vial. After considerable difficulty with the cork, due to the increased pressure at this depth, I liberated him, and my ego was pleased to see him streak for the surface. I felt more at home than before, and hailed the sand gobies and blue surgeons and emerald parrots as brethren of the same caste as I — we who could make our way far below where *Bathygobius soporator* was comfortable. Such is submarine snobbishness!

Lizard-fish and other sand-colored friends lived about me on the ocean floor, but as I sat quietly, unexpected visitors sometimes passed, paying no attention to this harmless projection seated in midsand, periodically spouting a geyser of bubbles. Without warning, two fish came toward me, side by side, each well over three feet in length, graceful and of superb beauty. They were yellow-tails — oxidized silver, with a broad golden band along the sides. A yellow-tail twelve inches in length is a large yellow-tail to the Bermudian angler. These giants had small, high-bred heads, arched backs and toward the tail their bodies narrowed like an athlete's waist, and behind all there waved a mighty reversed crescent of a tail. Their movements were effortless, their path in life was assured, their desires distinctly attainable — they know their stuff. For several yards they swam evenly, unhurriedly, then, one after the other, like perfectly synchronized parts of a single bit of mechanism, they dipped to the sand, each scooped up a great mouthful, and on the rise, sent it out in a flurry like dense smoke. Again and again they dipped and puffed, dipped and puffed, until in their wake there was a score of fading gouts of sand — like the vanishing sky blossoms of shrapnel smoke.

These and many others were passing visitors to my island, not to be watched for, because their size was unimaginable, their occupation unforeseen, their very presence wholly unexpected. Others were such permanent residents that I have named localities for them, such as Lobster Alley and Chub Canyon. Our pet lobster is of unusual size, and her antennae are forever protruding from the window of her apartment, well up on a reef-wall within a side canyon. Now and then I tweak her horns as I pass and she withdraws in insulted haste.

In Chub Canyon six or eight enormous chubs are always to be found. I do not think that a chub four feet over all has ever been captured in these islands, but here they are; records which would make an angler wild with envy.

With the water clear and free from sand and no fish as far as the eye could see, I once stooped at the foot of the ladder to pick up a net. As I straightened up I got the most terrific shock I can remember under-seas, for at first glance I seemed to be completely enclosed by some creature of enormous size. Within a second my eye had resolved the mass into hundreds upon hundreds of chubs, all about a foot in length, which had materialized in mid-water from nothing, and now swam so close that they shut out reef and sand, many of them almost within arm's reach — milling around and around me, apparently absorbed in interest in this being new to their cosmos. After several minutes another idea imbued the thousands, and as one fish, they turned and swam unhurriedly out and around the end of the reef. Five minutes passed before I began my ascent; the experience was too wonderful, the memory too vivid, to be immediately disturbed.

I am amused to find that I have described the inhabitants of my island as living on sand or reef, and omitted the water itself where the vast majority spend their lifetime. At certain seasons creatures appear who have nothing whatever to do with coral, reef or sand. In September, when flocks of shore birds migrate to the beaches of Nonsuch, schools, or more properly, sheer hosts of individual creatures far different swim into my ken; the passing, day after day, of great sun-jellies. They are so evanescent when viewed from below that I often detect them first by their shadows pulsating unevenly over the sand furrows — shadows which seem to possess more substance than their makers. When I am making my way with my arrows across a wide stretch of sand I sometimes leap up eight or ten feet and impale one of these great living plaques, thrusting my lance through and through the creature, a submarine pigsticking of sorts. It is a tribute to the simplicity of the nervous system of jellies that they appear to be quite unaware that anything untoward has happened to their machinery, and vibrate calmly on, after the manner of all healthy jellyfish.

A fine white strand drifts across the glass of my helmet and I reach out and brush it casually aside. But it is no derelict bit of seaweed, for at my touch it curls and twists and withdraws upward. I sight along its slanting length and high overhead, just dimly visible, at least thirty feet away near the surface, is a great Cyanea jelly, a half-bushel mass of deep lavender. As I look, it gently sinks and comes nearer, and I see the medusa head of a myriad tendrils. I side-step to avoid them for they sting severely, and with the sun behind me I detect a crowd of little fish scurrying in and out of the deadly portières. At that moment a black net filled with air bubbles appears and the jelly vanishes — my assistant has captured it, and we find that its attendant fish are little bumpers, quite new to Bermuda. Thousands of them spend their early life in these gorgon heads, generations having drifted for centuries past the Somers Isles without a single individual being cast ashore.

The first thing which questioners wish to know, and the last which occupies our minds, is the Dangers of Almost Island. Barracudas nose about us now and then, sharks but rarely in the daytime; morays of moderate length come to our bait and green chaps of embarrassing circumference and extent have their homes in the deeper wells, but only occasionally do we see their gasping jaws; groupers, as in Haiti, are sometimes a trifle too curious and fear-

9. Gurnet Rock. The water in the foreground covers Almost Island.

10. Gurnet Rock at night. At this time sharks come in by the hundred from the open sea.

less. So far, however, I have been attacked only by inchling demoiselles, when I have perched too near their chosen domicile, although sergeant majors now and then harmlessly nip at ankle or elbow. I shall write nothing in detail about so-called man-eaters and others; suffice it to say that I and my associates go down month after month, scores of times, and are too much enthralled by the interest and beauty and the never-ending strangeness of it all to give a thought to possible dangers.

Dangers, that is, from the creatures of the sea. Mechanical hazards are different. With unrelaxed vigilance we watch each diver and apparatus, and it is seldom that anything goes wrong. Once an inexperienced person in the helmet snagged the hose behind a projecting branch of coral, and, thinking that the tightening of the hose was the push of the tide, fought back to the ladder. There was fortunately sufficient length to allow an approach to within three feet of the surface, when we were able to reach the helmet. If this had not been possible, one of us would have dived and pulled off the helmet in mid-water, forcing the diver to swim to the surface.

Two or three times in spite of our care one of the leading ropes of the launch has become untied or broken. Instantly three sharp jerks on the hose tell that something is wrong. The last time this happened I was perched twelve feet up on the reef edge. I jumped to the open sand and saw the launch drifting rapidly over the reef, the ladder already hung up on a rock. I was afraid to use it, for fear of its snapping or of catching my hand between it and the reef. So I pulled the hose down until it became taut, and wrapping the loose coils about me, I cached my arrow-sling and net, and went swiftly up hand over hand, obliquely over the reef, attended by an excited mob of abudefdufs and surgeons. An anchor carried out to mid-sand in the glass-bottom dinghy enabled me to free the ladder, salvage my weapon and resume my hunting.

As once before in Haiti I caught my ankle in a crevice of Almost Island — a diabolically ingenious tie-up which compelled my sitting still and overcoming a momentary impulse to tear loose. When I had stopped unnecessarily using up the precious air in the helmet, I set systematically to work, and after trying every kind of push and pull and compression, and going through another unpleasant moment, I twisted around to bend my arrow and use it as additional leverage, when suddenly my ankle slipped out.

The coming of night to Almost Island deserves a chapter, or if we knew even a fraction of the great changes which every evening brings, an entire volume. The setting sun gives way to blue, always blue blackness, the movement of one's hand sets fire to a thousand luminous creatures in mid-water; many of the day-loving fish go to sleep in amazing positions; the big-eyed squirrel-fish and the sinister morays come forth, and the sharks begin to work their way in from the open sea. A sight I shall not forget is that of a dead horse which we tied to the western buoy, and at sunset Almost Island was alive with sharks. There were dozens of the four-foot puppy sharks which are so common about Nonsuch, and now and then I caught a glimpse of the white belly of one much larger, as it twisted up from below to share the feast. The next morning the horse had disappeared, not a shark was in sight, and over the spot five angelfish swam lazily, their golden filaments streaming out behind — the usual peace of early morning had returned to Almost Island.

The supreme achievement in helmet diving is Dangling, and I do not think this word has been used so appropriately before. The sea must be calm and without much swell and there must be a slight offshore breeze. On the last day of this combination I went out in the launch, beyond Gurnets, perhaps a quarter of a mile. Usually I try to see bottom but if the water is slightly murky or cloud shadows are frequent this is impossible. When I thought we were over a suitable place the engines were shut off, and I let out the entire forty-five feet of ladder, and started down.

In September the water is warm and fish life is at its greatest abundance. Peering down I could see nothing but a foggy blueness — it looked as if I were dropping off the rim of the world into starless naked space. I had no feeling of bottom at all; it was a real connecting link between my Almost Island meanderings and the miracle of view from the Bathysphere, two hundred fathoms down. I stopped

51

halfway, swung around and found myself clear off
in cosmic space. There was no sign of reef below or
boat or surface overhead; I was too close to the
ladder to see them, so I was apparently suspended in
mid-ether; a cloud shut out the sun for the moment
and the dusk was eery — unlike any earthly twilight. The fog-blue spaces swirled past; I could actually see thinner and denser areas, probably the
shift of light from the face of the wave mirrors high
overhead. I swivelled half a circle and entered a
galaxy — a whole constellation of great jellyfish.
Aurelias they were, sun-jellies, but a much more
appropriate term would be Lunelias, for they were
grey and misty. Two and thirty of these active
moons, all more than a foot across, throbbed around
me, set at all angles, each with a quartet of bright
pink loops at its center — egg-masses, insurance
of future generations of sun-jellies. One bumped
against the glass of my helmet, and before it could
regain equilibrium I reached out and held it balanced. Two or three tiny fish dashed away, and in
its watery tissues I could see small crustaceans, em-
bedded like flies in amber — parasites in a living
film of water. The delicate fringe of tentacles waved
about my face more gracefully than cobwebs could
in air. There came to me a profound feeling of the
permanence of the evanescent; these one-half of
one per cent of life filling the ocean with their
myriads, with adequate provision for the future —
each jelly perfect; and I knew that the first news-
paper I would open on my return would be an al-

most pure culture of worry, fear, danger, warning, despair. None of us wish to be " spineless jellyfish " but here was I, held fascinated by the marvel of their form and movement, and wishing for us a little of the calm and assurance of their lives.

Half a dozen more rungs brought the bottom into clear view, and now I slid slowly down until I grasped the lowermost, swung my feet and legs free in mid-water, and — *Dangled.* There had been a very light breeze in the upper world when I left and I found that I was hardly moving, drifting very slowly seaward. Within my forty or fifty feet horizon all was one tumult of tortured rock, — caves, gullies, slender arms of stone reaching out toward me, deep unsounded wells, galleries winding in and out — everything except a bit of flatness. I saw a great round mass slowly approaching and soon I was able to stand upright on a mighty brain coral. I laughed a hollow, coppery laugh all to myself in my helmet at the thought of my resemblance to Gulliver, only here I was perched upon the cranium of a giant who must have been a genius, with an appalling amount of convolutions showing clearly through his skull. I was gently tipped off during my momentary amusement and again I dangled.

The next projection was an angled bit of stone overgrown with seaweeds and plumes. While in temporary possession I danced vigorously upon it, kicked and stamped and scraped, and my reward for the next few minutes after I was plucked from it was a school of fifty golden wrasse dashing about the disturbed débris until they reminded me of the kaleidoscope of silver wires of moonlight on water. The sun was out full strength and against the dark rocks and weed the little fish shone like fire. As I drifted out of sight I could see the forms of larger creatures moving toward the unexpected manna. If I derived any satisfaction from being a freak pioneer, I could boast that I was the first human being who had fed fishes by dancing on coral tops eight fathoms down!

These open-sea danglings were like looking through a magnifying glass — the coral heads were so much more massive, the plumes taller, the fish so considerably larger than those of the inshore reefs; blue surgeons and angelfish, giant butterflies, parrots over four feet, and other fish in proportion. Now and then I see a species new to our list or even to Bermuda, some of which will always remain unknown to me, others recognizable on sight.

Toward the end of this particular dangle, my drifting speed increased; the wind in the upper world was evidently rising. I swept past jagged ridges and deep, dark valleys, and then came sand twenty feet farther down, next an island, and more sand. Suddenly a jagged crest appeared ahead. I scrambled hastily up half a dozen rungs and prepared to pull up the ladder after me. The only real danger of this work is that of the lower part of the metal ladder catching on some out-jutting finger and snapping in two or at the surface. I was constantly on the watch for such a catastrophe, hoping to be able in time to pull the ladder clear of the passing danger. In the event of its happening, the only thing to do would be to leap clear of the ladder and go hand over hand up the hose.

My ridge proved to be the last projection I could reach, and far from its catching on the ladder, I found I could only touch here and there by dangling full length, straight down from the lowest rung. Beyond lay a valley of shadows, then more sand, and my last view showed two grandfathers of all groupers, at least six feet in length, turning slowly and looking up at me. I had a moment's wild desire to let go and try to cross the sandy deserts and clamber the intervening reef mountains between me and Almost Island a quarter mile away. Then I remembered my limitations and ceased wishing to impose too great a strain upon my wonderful relations with the sea.

I climbed leisurely, my body and legs floating out behind, and again passed through the zone of star dust and Aurelias, and before I knew it the helmet was whisked off, I was asked what I had seen, and at once the perfection of my inarticulate visions began to be dissected and distorted by being forced into the pitifully inadequate vehicle of human speech and writing.

CHAPTER IV

AN old tale runs that a sailor returned to his mother with marvelous stories of what he had seen in foreign places. "There be one country," he said, "where all the rivers run milk by day and honey by night, and tobacco grows in thick squares of bark all ready to be prised off and chewed."

"My! My! Son, that do be wonderful. I would like to see that land," answered his mother.

"And there be waters where fish not only do leap out about the bows of the ship but spread wings and go flying over the water," continued the sailor.

And with that the irate parent thrust her son out of doors and bade him never come back, for any evil being who could so insult her with such obvious lies about impossible things was no son of hers.

And this is the mood in which we should approach our quest for flyingfish. Before we have ever seen one alive we should, as I have advised in the case of hummingbirds, active volcanoes and the rings of Saturn, preserve a gentle skepticism. Not an active, argumentative disbelief, but a childish doubt in reading of them whether these things are not too wonderful to be real.

This produces two worthy results: It keeps alive

a restless urge to see flyingfish for oneself, thus hopelessly destroying any suburban content with travel books and lectures; and it provides a greater impetus of appreciation, a deeper, more heartfelt spontaneity, whose satisfying chant at the supreme moment of direct realization may be voiced in the sentence, " By Jove! There really are flyingfishes! " How heartily Roosevelt concurred in this when I was with him years ago on a trip to South America; to explode the gentle, consciously hugged doubts in such dynamic fashion, rather than by the bored, life-weary, " What, flyingfishes? Oh, yes; Ananias Ulysses Methuselah writes about them in his books. I didn't see them myself, but they should have occurred about here. I must note it in my journal."

It is hardly possible to make the trip from New York to Bermuda without becoming convinced of the reality of flyingfishes. This is borne in upon the least observant tourist, even upon the poor wretches who look upon the living sea only during the dummy intervals of a bridge game.

From Nonsuch we may begin our actual quest in several ways, of which I will choose the most exciting. At sunup — or more correctly, earthdrop — we look out to sea and perceive a perfect day; the water is only slightly ruffled and here and there are slicks, calm as the surface of a mirror. After breakfast we take small boat and outboard motor, and, after the usual amount of top spinning and appropriate language, the absurd propeller begins to turn and we head around the island through Nonsuch

Scaur out to the east of Gurnet Rock, and the boat rises gently, curves over a great, slow-heaving hill and slides ever so smoothly into the next mobile valley. Ocean is quite asleep, with only the regular rhythm of her mighty swells to differentiate her from a Brobdingnagian mill pond.

I grasp the bow line tightly, forming a tripod with my two, widespread legs, and, standing as high as possible, watch for an inviting slick.

On we go, a half mile, eight, even ten furlongs. (I had to look this up as I had no idea how far a furlong was, except that horses won and lost races running them. Follow my example and you will know how far from shore was my flyingfish slick.)

We slowed down and stopped in the center of a smooth lane which ran, slightly meanderingly, east and west to the limit of my six-foot elevation of powers of perception. The sculling oar turned us lengthwise of this ocean lane, and slowly we crept along it. Although so far from land, there was only fifty feet of water, and I could distinctly see the coral and rock, sea-fans and sand beneath our keel.

I crouched in the bow and with an effort focused my eyes on the middle distance, on the intangible surface. Again and again they reshifted and I would discern the slowly unrolling panorama of the bottom, or by surface reflection my own eager face would be envisaged, always surrounded with the marvelous aureole of light rays. Finally the surface became more concrete; I concentrated on the living, floating dust, and the water assumed an appearance of solidity which left me no adequate reason for not stepping over the gunwale and walking off. With such a halo as I perceived when I saw the vision of myself I could surely attain the aquatic pedestrian ability of Saint Peter.

Although the slick was so wide, there was very little sargassum weed in it — a patch here and there with a multitude of isolated berrylike floats. In the slight wash of our slow-moving boat these bobbed about, which was natural and to be expected; but as I watched, net in hand, for the appearance of some fish, I saw two berries behaving as no proper sargassum berries should. They anticipated the bow ripple, and bobbed and moved before they or any other member of the vegetable kingdom had any right to. The suspicions of naturalists and policemen are always easily aroused, and nervous, acrobatic berries appealed to my collecting instinct as keenly as veritable fish. So I scooped one up, washed him into a bottle and saw my first, wild-caught, newly hatched flyingfish.

The scales now fallen from my eyes, I became more exocœtropic — which means that I went after my infant flyingfish with renewed enthusiasm born of increased intelligence. Within five minutes I learned why naturalists are acutely conceited and chronically humble, for I skillfully captured and bottled five perfectly good sargassum berries and allowed four of the fish mimics to pass out of reach.

Somewhat larger flyingfish now appeared, about a third of an inch in length, slightly too elongate to

sustain properly the berry camouflage; and with
the passing, the outgrowing of this protection, Nature — for lack of some better, very wonderful, all-
inclusive word — instantly offered compensation.
Even in this slight advance in age, the pectoral fin
had pushed out sufficiently so that the tiny fish
could not only rush a foot or two over the surface
of the water but actually leap in the air and scumfish
along for a foot.

One of my assistants made the suggestion that it
was getting late and the slick seemed to be petering
out, and a glance at him showed that far from any
intended pun, it was the slow lift and settle of the
gently rolling boat which prompted the tactful and
hopeful information. I took pity on the patient suf-
ferer and we started for home.

I found I had captured all three important stages
of the berry mimics, jolly little chaps, the largest
much less than an inch in length, the smallest only
one-sixth of an inch. Yet all performed separate
and individual actions suited to their particular
needs. All were reddish amber in color, exactly like
the sargassum berries. The smallest had still a fair
amount of yolk which rounded him out into berry
shape. His pectoral fins, potential wings, were very
short, hardly 15 per cent of his length, quite hyaline
and wholly useless for flight. When he was frightened he did exactly the same thing which he did
when he was calm and happy — he did nothing, just
like the berries. Flyingfishlet No. 2 was a trifle
larger, sufficiently unberrylike, as I have observed,

to make it wise to wriggle away from scientists with nets in motorboats, or any other dangers which fate might have in store. His wings were speckled with black and a third as long as his entire body. Fish No. 3 was almost a third of an inch in length, with jet-black wings, measuring 35 per cent of his whole length, and he could rise and skim the surface for a foot at a time — differing in degree only from the volant ability of his parents.

I watched their method of swimming and found that progress through the water was by violent vibration of the tail, and, to my surprise, with equally rapid movements of the pectorals as well, both fins moving simultaneously. The ventrals were left spread but quite motionless. So here was our catch — little amber-hued beings, speckled with black, with enormous eyes and wing fins that we could almost watch grow.

Thus I studied for a while in the laboratory and under the microscope my agile little fish, and then I became very unscientific and unreasonably enthusiastic. As many thousand times in my life before, and I hope at least another thousand times to come, my mind was simply satiated with the joy of perfect adaptation of form, pattern, color and movement to splendidly necessary ends. And I promptly walked to the south porch, climbed the railing and looked out at the lanes upon lanes of successive slicks from Gurnet to the horizon and thought of the myriads of infant flyingfish carrying on their new lives, hedged by instinct, guarded by thoughtless wisdom, steering perfectly between undue precociousness and fatal lagging in the scheme of behavior to which inheritance and adaptation had molded them.

Slicking for flyingfish far out at sea is a very different thing from running out a mile from shore to the nearest smooth patch. We can indulge in this sport only in the very rare days when the entire ocean is calm, with no ripples, but only the great ceaselessly heaving swells. We steam ten miles offshore on the tug until Bermuda becomes a mere dark ruled line along the horizon, bounded by the two infinitesimal nodes which are lighthouses. The Gladisfen dips and rises on each swell, making the motion much more apparent than it is to the eye, and our wake is the principal disturbance in the whole ocean.

When the two miles of wire are out and the deep-sea nets down and the long period of watchful waiting begins, on such a day of calm we launch the rowboat. This must be done with speed and skill, for at the least carelessness the boat would be crushed under the counter as the tug rolls from side to side. We push off and to my surprise the movement of the water almost ceases. The swells are so long that the rowboat slips over them unnoticeably. An ocean liner would probably wallow. Only if one watches the skyline does one realize the full movement, as the horizon is raised high above or settles far below. The rhythm shifts us from the bottom of a great bowl of polished ultramarine to the summit of a hill of sheer lapis lazuli.

One day in mid-June we headed aft a mile to a great field of seaweed. The faint breath of air which had arisen was perceptible only where it evanescently feathered the surface, leaving here and there great arenas, or long lanes of slick.

As I stood in the bow and looked down, the sun's light radiated as usual from my center of vision and so clear was the water and so profound the sense of materiality of the rays, that it seemed as if a dive would shoot me down a never-ending cone, waterless and lined with the blue-grey, velvety bars of light.

These slicks were not phenomena of an hour or a day, for some of them contained vast masses of sargassum weed, floating berries, rounded heads with sprouting fronds reaching up out of the water, or solid mats many yards across. Some slicks had no trace of weed, and yet their edges were as sharp as if made by some real barrier. Probably the weed which had oiled such an area had died and begun its slow submergence.

We traveled fast at first, the outboard motor going full speed, and when we reached the slick, we found that we had to deal with inchling or even larger flyingfish, and must develop a wholly new technique from that used near shore. It was tremendously exciting and reminded me of nothing so much as Ben Hur driving his chariot. Other similes might be pigsticking from a stand on horseback, or butterfly catching from a surf-board. Anyway, it was grand sport, all the more because we knew so little about the lives of these fish and every capture was a real addition to knowledge.

My companion, from his seat in the stern with the engine, depended on me for direction, and as I stood braced on the bow thwart, I had not only to hold to the taut bow line for support but watch for the young fish as they took to wing, indicate their line of escape, shout directions as to speed, and finally swing the net and capture my game either as it rose for a second flight or prepared to dive. When a particularly fine specimen ducked into the water and rose again at right angles, then when we banked sharply for the turn, and an unexpected swell carried us up toward the sky on an actively moving hillside, it took all my power of balance and poise to keep from following my game headlong into the sea.

Long ago on the Arcturus I gave the name of butterflyingfish to some brightly colored young ones, and here in these northern waters they more than ever deserved the title. We caught hardly two alike and none was somber. While we are quite ignorant of the whole life histories of these fish, yet these gorgeously pigmented youngsters seem to represent intermediate stages between the amber and yellow colored, newly hatched young which probably owe their existence through a stage of infantile helplessness to sargassum berries, and the protectively colored ultramarine and silver full-

64

11. Looking down through the ceiling of Almost Island to the
brain corals and seafans of the reef floor.

12. Four tenants of Almost Island: Abudefdufs, a Striped Grunt and a Blue Surgeon.

grown fish. The great variety of pattern and color in the same species, and their continued proximity to the sargassum weed, hint that the shift of hue and shadow, and the parti-colored parasitic growths on this weed must be a valuable protection, in addition to the activity in sea and air of the fish themselves.

Some of the little chaps have red bodies, others red and yellow, either fore-and-aft patterns, or a succession of red bands. The wings may be solid chocolate-brown, black or mottled, or variegated with scarlet, white, blue and gold. They often show colors and patterns as soft and delicate as those of great moths, and, like some of those insects, the brilliant hues are invisible in the closed wings and flash out only when the fins are spread in flight.

Another delicate refinement of adaptation was exhibited by a different species of young flyingfish. These were few in number, small, and quite pale, chiefly with transparent wings touched with blue. They were to be seen only in the slicks barren of weed and, guided by an infallible, inherited instinct, they would have nothing to do with the floating meadows. True to their pigment, they preferred the open sea, and flew out and away when frightened. If they were to win through and live it must be by kindness of the open sea and sky.

At this stage — one to two inches — these young flyingfish exhibit another feature as unexpected as their rainbow hues. From the front and sides of the lower jaw fleshy barbels or aprons grow out —

most astonishing structures, sometimes slender and barbule-like, or again like a pair of fleshy fans wide-spread as we look at the fish head on. I can think of several reasons, such as increased friction and overconspicuousness, why these should not exist, but I cannot offer a single reason or explanation for their presence.

Later we found that we could bring down medium-sized fish with .22 caliber shot cartridges, but the chase with the net was much more sporting and less damaging to the specimens.

After an hour of pursuit and capture, we killed the motor and drifted quietly in the heart of a field of weed. For the first time in my life I realized what a place of absolute silence is mid-ocean on a day of calm. Always at sea one is accustomed to hear the throbbing of the engines, or wind in the rigging or flapping of sails or eternally the chatter of fellow humans. Here we floated in perfect silence — an unbroken stillness amid the golden weed deep in a hollow of ocean walled with water for yards above our heads, or balanced, still in a breathless hush, poised on a motionless swell high in air with the horizon broken only by the tug, half hidden a mile away. Then gently again down, down, down.

I leaned far over the bow with my ear close to the weed and heard the only sound in all the miles around — two little crabs had climbed up on a sargassum sprout and were sucking audibly at the water in their gills. Then somewhere in the next valley or two a whale spouted, sighed and sank quietly. We glimpsed the drifting spray in the air on the next rise. The crabs climbed down again, and for many minutes there was unbroken silence. The quiet filled our thoughts; one of us whispered very low and the other merely nodded in answer. Our ears strained pleasantly and we found vibration only through the eye and the lulling sensation of the rhythmic rise and fall, rise and fall, of the whole visible universe.

So through the day we put-putted from slick to slick. When our bottles were filled and the gasoline got low, we returned abreast the tug and on ahead, so that if our motor should go dead we could row to our mother ship. We were about twelve miles out, and a tropicbird passed us, flying still farther seaward in search of his meal of squids. Then the wave of a hand from one of our crew sent us far out to starboard. Soon we saw a large black bird resting buoyantly on the water. It rose as we approached, and as I did not recognize it I shot it — a pomarine jaeger, a bird of the year, hatched probably in Central Greenland and now wandering southward on the beginning of its migration.

A pair of whales blew and blew some distance away, tall fountains of spray rising and drifting into invisibility, like some strange geyser from a heaving plain of limpid lava. The idea would not leave us that it was perfectly possible to step overboard, walk off and tow the boat. It seemed as if we almost had sufficient faith.

Halobates, the only insects that have mastered the open ocean, were in the slicks in small numbers, and linked them closely with the land, just as last night on my laboratory table two little water boatmen came to my light and miserably rowed themselves about over the plate glass until I took pity and gave them a saucer of water. Theirs is a brave spirit. It seems absurd to think of bugs as admirable explorers, yet it is *Halobates,* and *Halobates* alone, which can penetrate the most distant waters of the Atlantic and the Pacific and call them home.

When at last we turned back to the tug, eight blackfish whales rolled and curved across our path like ancient, rheumatic dolphins. When still fifty yards off, all rose a little higher than usual, bent into eight segments of circles and unhurriedly but effectively vanished forever. There was no splash, only eight small slicks marking the spot where dozens of tons of small whales had sunk. The smoothness spread and spread, and finally coalesced, and then our motor's wake tore it into shreds of foam.

In sargassum weed there lives a fish so like the fronds and berries in shape and color and pattern that we almost credit the goose-barnacle story of medieval times — that proper birds and animals can spring full-grown from plants and barnacles and such. And when a nest of many small fish eggs was found in the weed, the inference was obvious. Sixty years ago, Louis Agassiz reported this tale of the frogfish, or *Pterophryne,* and since then only poor

13. The author studying fish, four fathoms under sea.

Painting by Else Bostelmann.

14. Pempherids inhabit Almost Island by the hundred.

compilers have failed to include the fact in text-book or fish volume. As long as I can remember I have been on the lookout for a nest of this kind and I can never resist picking up any rounded mass of gulf weed, whether on sea or shore.

Five times I have found these nests of eggs in compact balls of weed. The first three I accepted with no more misgiving than a medieval monk would doubt the dictum of Aristotle. In the fourth all the eggs were dead, but an advanced embryo showed no hint of resemblance to a frogfish or any of its relations. The fifth was taken as we returned from a long day in the slicks of mid-ocean off Nonsuch, and all the eggs were alive and vigorous.

The weed was tightly packed into a ball about four by five inches in diameter, and was held together by many very strong turns of white string. When cut, these contracted at once into a tangle of numerous fine, silken threads. The eggs were in three general stages of development, and when I unwound several feet I found that there were three separate masses of these stages, hinting strongly that three female fish had taken part in the laying. The most important thing was that each egg had a number of long, very thin hairs attached to it, a character peculiar to a family of fish which includes flyingfish. And in fact I was able to rear a number of the young fish to a stage where they were recognizable as flyingfish, and from a count of the rays of their fins we could even be sure that they were of the genus *Exonautes*. The eggs which I have found fully developed in adult frogfish show no trace of silken strands.

It is rather a pleasing thought that the fish which in method of progression most resemble birds should also build nests. The eggs in their earliest development were in the gastrula stage, which means that they somewhat resembled the adult condition of jellyfish, a stage through which fish and birds and ourselves have to pass. The easiest way to visualize it is to press in one side of a rubber ball until the two layers are close together in the shape of a hollow, two-layered cup.

I placed the eggs in an aquarium, gave them an abundance of oxygen, and they developed rapidly. In an astonishingly short time the little fish could be seen lying on top of an enormous mass of yolk, and day by day he grew larger until he was wrapped around half the circumference of the rest of the egg. This hollow world of his was less than a sixteenth of an inch in diameter, and yet within it he began to exercise many of the activities of his adult life.

First his eyes are dominant over all his being, then the brain case begins to pile up, something like a mouth appears, and large, branched bits of black and yellow pigment preface all the blazing colors of the adult. The heart is an open saclike affair through which we can see the colorless corpuscles being pumped rather slowly over the yolk and back. A day or two more and the heart has settled down to its life work, beating two and a half times a second, and the corpuscles are stained with orange.

Then the whole egg takes on the color of rust, and the microscope shows the blood quite red. Our flyingfish is getting restless and now and then gives a convulsive leap — sufficient, we should say, to destroy all the delicate membranes in the egg. But the special god of infant flyingfish knows his job, and early one morning we see a pair of perfectly good fins waving in mid-egg. The tail flicks about and the small fish actually revolves in its egg case — the yolk always growing less and the body of the fish larger. The wing fins flap alternately, first one and then the other. Even the jaws open and close slightly, and the eye has begun to function and a sudden flash of the light from the microscope mirror will cause the fish to flinch and often turn completely around.

Before it hatches, the fish has become greenish or yellowish orange, and the head has grown up to match the size of the eyes. The gills show regular breathing movements, and the embryo fits so tightly within the egg that the fins can no longer do more than wriggle at the base. Finally a supreme convulsive squirm breaks the barrier and the infant fish slips out into what to me is a watch glass on my microscope stage — to him it is his ancestral ocean. He stretches out his cramped body to full length — four millimeters, or a sixth of an inch. For a while he lies inert, borne down, if not by the realization of being at liberty on the face of our planet, then at

71

least by the shock of emergence and the weight of the remaining yolk. Then frenzy seizes him and with wild, uncontrolled movements of tail and fins he dashes from side to side of the dish, and when he comes to rest every movable part of him is oiled and working smoothly. The ventral fins, which were invisible in the egg, are going, the heart pumps madly, the gills are fluttering, the tail moves tremulously back and forth, the eyes roll slightly in their sockets and the mouth is taking in the life-giving fluid. Most interestingly, the movement of the pectoral or wing fins has changed from alternate to simultaneous, both beating at the same time, an approach to the steady, braced posture which very existence will demand from them in the future. Two days later and the anal fin shows rays distinct enough to count, and the number of fourteen together with other characters marks our young fish as *Exonautes rondeletii,* one of the four-winged flyingfish.

A flyingfish has been called a miracle, but only in early human history do miracles spring fullblown, like Jason's armed men, from beginnings or nothings. In the world of Nature miracle is only another way of spelling ignorance. We find that most of our flyingfishes' relations are of exceedingly active habit, jumping from the water upon the slightest provocation. The ferocious gars with their crocodilian jaws and teeth give such frenzied and undirected leaps that fishermen are sometimes maimed or even killed by the impact.

SLICKING FOR FLYINGFISHES

The skippers are more closely related to the flyingfish, and when hard pressed by bonitos or other enemies they leap out and flick themselves along above the surface by vibrations of the tail until they seem almost to be fully sustained by the air. Thousands of skippers thus jump out at once, presenting a most remarkable appearance. This method is exactly that of an aquaplane, shooting along obliquely by the thrust of the propeller. The nearest approach to flying is shown by *Euleptorhamphus* and the unrelated fresh-water flyingfish of South America. The latter skitter along, their sharp keel-like bodies trailing and leaving a narrow wake, while the former actually get up above the surface. From the point of view of comparative movement and emersion, these various examples are of interest, but they are end products and in no way explain the actual evolution of the real flyingfish. Fossil flyingfish are almost unknown, and only theoretically can we reconstruct the development through the ages from fin to wing.

The question of true flight versus gliding has been argued for a generation and has been settled conclusively. The flight of these fish is exactly like that of the gliders of human manufacture, where the impetus is given by a great elastic cord and the consequent progress and suspension are shared by the impetus and the upward pressure of the air. In the case of the man-made affair the impetus soon gives place to utilization of air currents, rising upward from valleys and slopes, while with the fish the impetus probably accounts for four-fifths and the air for only a small fraction of the suspension. There are muscles sufficient for spreading and closing the great expanse of web and rays, but none for vibrating or flapping. The wealth of ingenuity of Mother Nature is shown by the various groups of flyingfish, some gaining their object birdlike as monoplanes, with only a single pair of large pectoral or breast fins, while others are biplanes, with two pairs of fins developed. The law of compensation rules that these enlarged fins can play only a single part in the activities of the owner, and when a flyingfish swims it is by means of the tail fin alone, while the wings dangle helplessly, like half-closed fans.

The chief object of the power of flight is undoubtedly to escape enemies. As our steamer makes its way over the calm expanse of ocean, the surface seems to hide only great peace and quiet. We occasionally see fish swimming near the top, or whales rolling and spouting, or dolphins playing about the bow. But when in the distance a hundred silvery forms break forth and glide until gravitation pulls them back, we realize that the struggle for existence is as severe here as anywhere. With voracious fish always on the watch, the flyingfish need every inch spread of canvas and every turn of their little turbine tails that they can command.

Flyingfish are excellent eating and in places like Barbados their capture is a regular industry. During the day they have perfect control of body and fins whether in water or air, but at night, in the

circle of radiance of a light they are as helpless as
moths. Fishermen sometimes gather a full catch by
sitting quietly with a lantern in a boat while the
fish leap over and in of their own accord. I have
known them to strike the side of the Arcturus with
sufficient force to stun themselves, and have had
them fly into lighted portholes to the farther wall
of the cabin. They sometimes fall on the decks of
vessels many yards above the surface of the water.

Aside from this method of jacking, however, it
is far from easy to capture full-grown flyingfish. I
have succeeded in shooting them with a double-
barreled shotgun from the bow of a launch and
have found it the most exciting and difficult of
sports. When an area is reached which these fish
are known to inhabit, I brace myself as firmly as
possible and the launch is driven ahead full speed.
The flushing and shooting of pheasants and quail
is child's play in comparison, for here we have the
advance, pitch and roll of the boat, the flicker of
light on the ever moving waves, together with the
complete uncertainty of the direction of rise and
flight of the quarry. And hardest of all is the fact
that one shoots below the level of the shoulder, and
this demands a technique which is wholly alien to the
shooting of game birds.

A wing injury will generally cause the fish to dive
at once, before the launch reaches it, but at the
slightest nick of a shot pellet on the body it turns
over and remains quiet until scooped up in a net.

When I leave civilization and start out for some

of the rare remaining wild places of earth, there are one or two treasured stimulants of the senses — master sounds or smells or sights or tastes or touches — which serve to tear away the last barriers which cities and crowds have built up, and to reassure the feeling of intimacy which should never have been allowed to lessen. In a first approach to a New World jungle, satisfaction comes through the call of a kiskadee, a toucan, or a howling monkey; when great crashing breakers have become the thinnest of silvery silken threads, then I begin to have the feel of the air; when through the darkness comes the rich salty aroma of stranded seaweed, I possess the yet unseen shore and tidepools; as the first fish peers into my helmet and says " Oh! Oh! Brother! " the undersea is no longer alien; and finally, after hours of half-hypnotized watching of shining waves, when the first flyingfish in its brave armor of silver and ultramarine breaks through the surface, then all the mystery of ocean reaches deep into my soul and I am glad to be alive and filled with enthusiasm and the eternal desire to know.

15. Shooting flyingfish from the bow of the Skink.

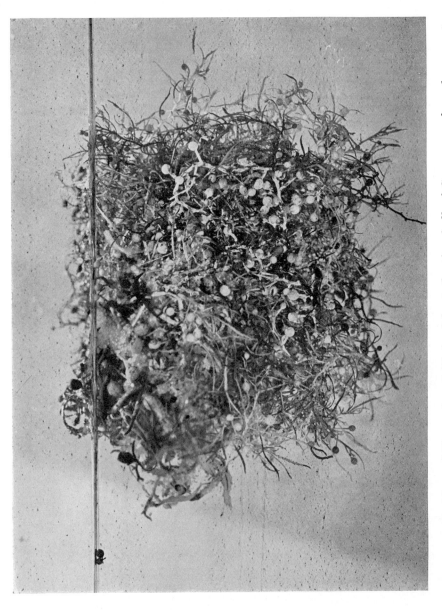

16. Nest of Four-winged Flyingfish. A floating ball of Sargassum bound together with silken threads.

CHAPTER V

THE edges and rims of things are much more exciting than the things themselves. This is true even of man's handiwork when he works for the love of the working — witness the glorious, cosmic-horizon, china rims of Ming tissue bowls.

As long as the planet Earth was covered by the waters these were monotonous and comparatively safe. But with the appearance of the first dry land, shores began to be. Up to this time fish and other sea creatures could enjoy their three planes of watery space, they could swim up, down and around, and when the active air made the surface unpleasant, they simply dived to calm.

All was changed with the coming of a shore. The stand-patters, to be sure, merely swam away from it, and to the flyingfishes, if there were flying-fish then, the shore meant nothing, for they must ever rise from and fall into the sea.

But out of hoi polloi, from protozoa to fish, there was, as please God there always will be, a moiety — a small glorious band disturbed by a blind, divine discontent, by unconsciously progressive guts, who gathered from far and near, and began an unending assault on this primeval shore, this new, amazing

77

rim of things. From that first dry land — shall we say a thousand million years ago — up to the present moment (which as I write goes to join the billion years) this contest has never ceased for a moment.

The thought comes to me that to keep from writing as a rank outsider, I should plunge into and pass through this battlefield unprepared, on the impulse of the moment. So I go.

I have just returned from my pragmatic experiment and I would not exchange the experience for anything. Just as the creatures of old had to make their first attack with their sea-evolved equipment, so it seemed fair for me to rise from my desk and walk straight down to the shore without preparation. This was not as drastic a performance as it sounds, quite unlike jumping off a high bridge in full evening dress for a bet, for on Nonsuch my costume consists of three articles of clothing — a woolen shirt, khaki shorts, and a pair of canvas sneakers.

As I rose from my table I could hear the surf booming on the rocks at the foot of the hillside of cedars. The day was sheer brilliant sunshine, hot and with very little breeze, but from some disturbance far to the south the rollers were piling in. I walked comfortably on the mat of soft needles and in the shade of dense foliage — I was a land mammal and this was my native habitat. Even so, the eons of years had left me only partly adapted to these haunts; if I looked intently at the sun I should be blinded, if I exposed my skin unwisely, the result would be an intolerable burn. Yet there were delicate adaptations for assurance of safety, such as the protective ochraceous tawny (by Ridgeway's Color Key!) of my skin at present.

I reached the last of the stunted cedars and walked among weeds — goldenrod and sea-lavender. Then I came to the end of the soil and the beginning of the naked rocks. The most casual onlooker could tell that I was getting beyond my natural environment, for I had to desert the upright bipedal locomotion of a Lord of Creation and clamber down on all fours. I had already passed beyond the permanent home of any true terrestrial animal, but here and there in sheltered hollows, where a handful of soil and débris had lodged, sturdy little sea-oxeyes fought for enough rain and sun to counteract the choking brine. Two feet below and to the left of the last of these green pioneers appeared a tiny basin of water. It was slimy and exceedingly hot, and a few drops on my tongue indicated a saturated salt solution. At times of storm or any high surf, such as five days ago, this cup was replenished by flying drops, and between storms slowly evaporated. It was lined with a dense, yellow-green nap of algae — as true seaweed as the sargassum a thousand miles from shore. I let myself down and stood with one hand on the silvery green foliage of the ox-eye, cousin of thistles, daisies, and goldenrod, and with my other I plucked tufts of seaweed, so close in physical space have the plants of sea and land approached.

I found an easier descent and climbed painfully over the needle sharp points, rough carved by the acids of the water and sharpened by the emery of shifting sand and wind. A projecting pinnacle gave suddenly and I tore my shirt and the skin within. As I approached the great curving, green surges my enthusiasm for a direct undeviating path became moderated, and crab-wise I sidled into a deep, narrow canyon floored with sand. At the moment I dropped to the welcome softness, a curling, roaring mass of foam and green shreds of water tore around a bend, undermined my footing as if it had been quicksand, and I was flung to my knees. I staggered upright, turned to offer my side to the wash, and instantly was buried in a smother of flying spume from the opposite direction, thrown back from the impact on the rocks. Nose, eyes, ears were filled with the stinging sand-roiled salt water and I climbed several feet up the sharp points to get my breath. The smashing blow and the rebound had come too quickly to be avoided, and the first round belonged quite conclusively to the sea.

Still preferring the sand-floored gully to a precarious, barbed-wire descent from a rock, I retraced my steps to the head of the narrow gorge and began anew, gripping the roughnesses as I walked knee-deep through the swirling half-sand, half-water. At every step I passed the tight-clinging, vacuumed limpets, winkles, and chitons, and here and there

17. Newly laid eggs of flyingfish in Sargassum weed.
Greatly enlarged photograph.

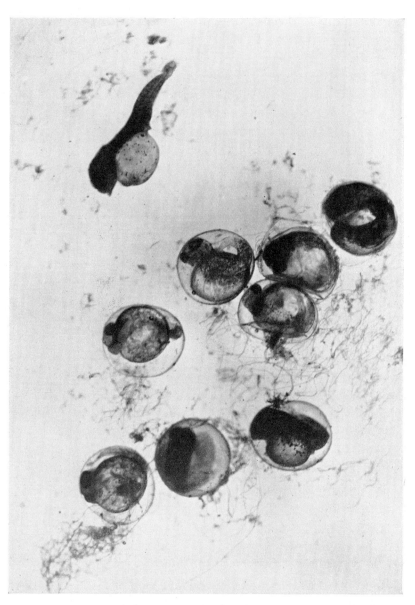

18. Eggs of flyingfish ready to hatch, and one newly-hatched fish.

clusters of small black mussels, anchored firmly in sheltered hollows. Close overhead swooped a pair of creaking tropicbirds, wheeling and circling in raucous protest at my too close approach to their young, undetectable, except to the sense of smell, at the end of some long, meandering tunnel.

I reached my cover safely, peered around it and instantly darted back, and tried to become a limpet, crab and mussel at once. It was no use. I was only a human being, quite out of place. My clothing kept catching on corners and I was again knocked off my feet. This time, like white mice and other higher terrestrial mammals, I had learned by trial and error, and did not fight against the backwash, but allowed it to sweep me around the corner in full view of the open sea. Another mighty roller was headed in, and met the backwash, and the two, after leaping high in air, sank rather quietly and quickly, leaving me limp and looking much like a drowned rat, braced with all my muscles against an impact which did not materialize. As result of this I pitched seawards and was rolled partly over, my side scraping against a submarine cross-cut saw of sorts. A lull ensued, so long that a dozen little fish came and dashed about excitedly, apparently wrought to highest pitch by the presence of my life blood diffused through the water.

I marched unsteadily onward and found a partly submerged reef just before the next wave came, and with its undertow I struck out strongly from shore. Twice I was carried back almost to the rocks a few yards farther east, then I reached the outer zone where the rollers only rose and fell, and the only unpleasant thing was the choppiness of the water. This slapped, slapped in my face, until I turned over and sculled with my hands.

A minute passed and I was considering returning, when I felt a rather sharp blow on the top of my head. This was quite new to my sea experience and I righted myself with utmost speed. There, staring with large, frightened eyes into mine, was a full-plumaged young tropicbird. I reached out toward it and it flapped helplessly a few times. It was evidently too water-logged to rise. This explained the daring swoops of the parent birds close over my head ever since I had reached the beach. Twice I swam with all my might toward the bird, but it avoided me easily. Its tail was raised and spread like the rays of a heraldic sun, but it gave forth no sound. Seeing the uselessness of further pursuit I turned and struck out for home. For the fraction of a second I had a sinking of the heart — the tide and what breeze there was, were against me, and the undertow was apparent if I lowered my feet even a little. The panic passed and in spite of my dragging clothes and shoes I knew I could certainly make it. So my mood changed to the appreciation of how completely I had made my point: The difficulty of adjustment, or in my case, readjustment to a strange element. Certain offshoots of my ancestors — whales, dolphins and seacows — had successfully achieved a return to aquatic life.

Here however was a tropicbird, essentially a being of the air, and a mammal of the land, both in trouble of sorts, due to maladjustment. I sculled and got my breath, and found myself at the outer line of foam. I had no trouble at first in getting in, once I secured a good grip on the rocks, but farther on a second bit of stone gave way and down I rolled, half buried in the smother before I could scramble a few feet higher. Here I made two brief stops, once to dig in as the water broke over me, and again when I reached a wide pool, freshened by every tide and full of the brave little gobies who had fought and won this great fight. When well out of the waves, I sat and got my breath back again, examined my wounds and wrung out my clothes, gradually assuming again the characteristics of a member of the terrestrial fauna of the globe.

I looked out at the young tropicbird bobbing up and down and realized that after all I was even more sharply set off from the creatures of the sea than my habiliments and unaquatic, inadequate limbs suggested — for my difficulty in getting inshore again, my temporary panic were due to my altruistic attempts to save the bird from what, sooner or later, must have been certain death. And this was a mental attribute which would never have worried any oceanic being trying in past ages to go terra firma.

In my laboratory I threw away my cheap, water-soaked watch and unlimbered another, dried my rust-proof knife, hung up my leather belt in the sun, and sent out a man in a boat to salvage the young tropicbird.

I am anxious to get down to the affairs of the creatures who are waging their shore conflict, but I keep wishing that someone would first write a most wonderful essay — a veritable saga — of this area from the point of view of the elements — the physics and chemistry of this most active, dynamic, pseudo-vital zone. Here we have a gas, a liquid, and a solid forever having it out, with force, movement, sound, victories and defeats, all of which would pass as organic in a hundred particulars.

The shore being what it is, a place unique, dramatic, of the greatest interest, it should not have to depend on any simile, however apt, any metaphor despite its appropriateness. Yet such is human frailty, with such mental difficulty can we set apart man's quarrels and nature's competitions, that the strife on the seashore for new opportunities, increased advantages in life, can be considered only in phraseology of warfare and battle. Once we yield to this temptation, the superficial resemblances become amazing.

From my desk I look down the south hillside of Nonsuch, over the solid ranks of goldenrod and between the gnarled cedar trunks to the heaving green waters. There is no scream of shells overhead but an almost continuous roar of the surf in my ears, not to be distinguished in memory from the sound of distant guns, as they came, night after night, to

Verdun, to Furcy and to Dunkirk. As I look I see fountains of spray shoot up into the air, like the return of material things to their native elements after a direct hit with HE. The shore is almost as bare of vegetation as were the fields about Douaumont, and the gradual approach of the tide, foot after foot, yard after yard, is the perfect parallel of a creeping barrage.

Now that we have labored our simile we might strive to realize the lack of changes in our shore-line since Cain killed Abel or the first apeman showed signs of progress toward humanity by fashioning a club and braining his neighbor.

Evolution is going on everywhere, but usually so quietly that we are not conscious of it. The turbulent warfare of elements and life on the seashore is so tempestuous that we cannot forget it. We may cut down trees and dig ourselves into cities on land, or we may travel in only slight peril of our lives from shore to shore across the ocean. But when all the wildernesses have been tamed, all the deserts made to grow food and clothing, cradles and coffins, the open shore-line will still be a wild place. Wharves and jetties and breakwaters may last for a time, but sooner or later, wind and wave will lift together and reduce them to sand and rust and splinters.

Let us take our stand on a cliff a few yards above the sea, with rocks to our right and a sandy beach to the left. We have here, on southeastern Nonsuch, a typical sample of the tens of thousands of miles of narrow shore ribbon which mosaics the surface of the globe. In the far north, to be sure, the water at times pretends to be solid like the real land, but that only means pushing the shore for a time farther out.

To have pass in review a résumé, a panorama of the daily and nightly rhythm of the meeting place of air, water and land, we should begin our watch at high tide, and if it is the time of the new moon the waters will be pulled to their maximum. On the beach the rollers break high, and the foam slithers up to the very foliage of the hardy shock troops of land plants. Sargassum weed is tossed about, great furrows are worn in the sand, visible momentarily, as an interval longer than usual between two waves sends the sand and water far out. Off the rocks the breakers sweep landward in low mounds, hardly perceptible at first; then rise higher and higher, finally curving in an endless length of crescent. For a terrible moment this hangs in midair before the tons of water crash down — splintering into an infinitude of drops and thinning the air into an agonizing vacuum which instantly is released in an explosion of sound — liquid on the shifting sands and a solid deep roar against the sounding board of the cliffs.

The wide zone between low and high tide marks is now all water and filled with watery beings. Great emerald and rufus, yard-long parrotfish are close inshore, wallowing on their sides, browsing among the waving banners of seaweed; I see a goatfish now and then sand-tapping for what-there-is for goatfish. Strange crabs and crayfish creep behind the incoming surges — camp followers picking here and there at stray corpses of things.

Six hours later everything is changed. The wind has gone down and the water — far out at lowest tide mark — laps against the rocks and slithers gently over a few inches of sand. Recalling conditions a quarter of a day before, there comes to mind the tricky arrangement I have seen in the store windows of a circular aquarium filled with swinging goldfish surrounding a space in which canaries fly about, so that to the eye of the onlooker fish and birds seem inextricably mingled in the same medium. Where sergeant-majors and parrotfish and wrasse wandered and browsed, turnstones, sandpipers, catbirds and sparrows now hop and fly and chase beach-fleas, a pair of silver-spotted butterflies flutter low over the sand, flies hover about the dead seaweed, a skink darts among the crevices and I myself creep down to the water's very edge. The fish have been forced back by the pull of the moon and in their place are representatives of the four great groups of land animals — insects, reptiles, birds and mammals.

I can find no words adequately to tell what this shift of creatures means to me but it has something in it of the deep significance of evolution, of the impersonal, inevitable rhythm of the inorganic, compared with the malleable adaptiveness of organic life. The point is wholly lost unless the entire phenomenon is considered simultaneously, — fish-crab-fly-sparrow-lizard-man-sand-rocks-water-air-moon; then we have it for a moment. It is almost immediately lost again, and our restless weakling minds reassume their myopic casualness, and we see only a fish, a wave, a bird, or a beach.

In war there are two major methods of attack, a frontal assault by sheer force, or a lateral movement, usually concealed as much as possible, which ultimately will develop into an attempt on the flank or even on the rear.

Let us go back sufficient millions of years to when most of the important groups of animals have become established in the sea and imagine the more adventurous spirits among them approaching this new thing — a shore. Most of the creatures, being Babbitts, or John Smiths or good middle-class peasants of the great marine democracies, never heard of the shore, or if they became conscious of it through what passed for movies in the Cambrian or wireless in the Ordovician, they shivered and gave thanks that they did not have to leave their abyssal hearths for any such new-fangled resorts. The gloriously discontented aforementioned few, however, began their attack and to this day are still continuing it.

Their early success proved to be their ultimate failure to achieve land life. Their story is comparable with an expedition which sets out to explore a swamp-surrounded desert, and the members of which become so skilled in conquering the difficulties of swamp that they expire in the heat of the desert's sun.

BATTLEFIELD OF THE SHORE

The floating population of the incoming tide is of indirect but of great importance to our shore zone. No tide ever goes out that it does not leave at least one stranded and wrecked jellyfish on the sand. Of all aquatic beings this is the most wholly unadapted to a life in any other element. We see one of these beautiful creatures throbbing slowly through the water — a round transparent or translucent sun, with disk, vein-like channels, tentacles, poison darts, eye-spots, nerves, mouth, stomach, eggs — every mechanism of life, and an hour later a thin, glairy, glistening film on the sand is all that is left. That we are three-fourths water is marvel enough, but the living, active, successful race of jellies is only one half of one per cent animal matter.

The thought of a jellyfish coming ashore and running on the sand or scampering up the rocks on the tips of its tentacles is worthy of a place only in a fantasy of Dunsany. A still wilder and more fantastic tale could be written of a jelly which, envious of a shore life and aware of its own watery quintessence, regards the success of the fast-rooted seaweeds and thereafter deposits eggs which hatch and sprout into comely plants whose fruit is piles of infant jelly saucers. Only in this case, the tale, censored of anthropomorphic allusion, is a scientific truth. A jelly can never learn anything of static seashore life, but its mother and its daughter — hydroids we call them — might tell it much about the rhythmic swing, back and forth, of waves crashing in, and all that has to do with tides.

NONSUCH

Early in the shore assault, the impetuous shock troops having won an advanced position dug themselves into such concrete bomb-proofs that they have never been able to get out — either to advance or retreat, and there they are today, splendid examples of over-specialization. And not one group but many have thus fallen and taken root by the wayside. Next to jellies, sea anemones would seem to be the most susceptible to unusual outer obstacles, yet here and there on the rocks I find colonies of these wine-colored blobs of hardened jelly, whose resistance to injury from the elements, compared with jelly-fish, is as rubber to cobwebs.

Advance scouts of crustaceans have won to success, such as crabs and pill-bugs, but barnacles are shut-ins, forever cribbed and confined between tides. As an esquimo can fish through the floor of his igloo if built on the ice, so barnacles at times of flood reach out through the roof of their marble wigwams and hook in passing bits of food.

The great race of snails has won a step farther on. After hatching they find some quiet place, and set up a lime kiln and devote themselves to architecture. By subtle alchemy of glands they magic imitation rocks from the invisible water, and mould them on the potter's wheel of their own bodies. Then the limpets and the chitons wage their life war, and advance over the rocks like a battalion of diminutive tanks, — taking shelter in a vacuum-rooted immobility under stress of waves, and moving slowly about when hungry. Even the mussels, apparently moored for life by a nexus of silken cables, can cut those farther aft, and throw out fresh ones forward and to starboard, and so warp themselves slowly toward the promised land. We might go on through the whole animal kingdom, and find still more exciting units in the front-line trenches. And always we must credit these pioneers with having solved in this maelstrom zone all the primary problems of existence — the finding and securing of a foothold, sufficient oxygen in water or air, safety from enemies, access to and ability to woo a mate, and nursery sanctuary for their offspring.

Tidepools are both a source of help and an added scene of difficulties. When the tide goes out they remain as a welcome oasis — for them tides do not exist. But when a warrior from the sea puts his trust in them he finds his troubles multiplied — the sun pours down and heats the water beyond all bearing, or the rain changes them from salt to brackish, and from brackish to fresh. Or if they are very high upon the rocks they become stagnant between spring tides.

Tidepools raise false hopes which end all progress. For fish like gobies they have always been a welcome halfway house of rest — a littoral dâk bungalow — but so pleasant withal that these and other fish have lingered in them too long. They are inured to fresh water, to excess of heat, to stagnancy, but to maintain themselves they have sacrificed their nether paired fins to the fashioning of a vacuum cup, and thus ended all hope of future legs.

So however we may rightly admire the amazing
adaptations and nice adjustments of the shore folk
to their difficult haunts of life, yet we see that if life
on land was their goal they are all failures, and
we see no answer to our own evolution. In their own
field, however, let us continue to think of them as
supreme, as absolute victors, and not forget the
thousands and thousands of other attempts which
failed and were blotted from our knowledge.

What about the flank or rear attack which we
mentioned? While the brilliant courageous cam-
paigns were going on along the sea front, there
were, in ages past, side lagoons, salt marshes and
mud holes scattered in bays and hinterlands of the
shore. Mud-loving fish wallowed and slithered their
way through the slime and shallow water, consoli-
dating first of all lung-like structures which could
use the oxygen of the air. Then, pottering about
and continually lifting their heads to gulp air, their
fins assumed more and more the nature of feet, and
soon they were rather amphibian than fish. Some
as usual became too good amphibians, and hence
the frogs and toads of today, with their fishy tad-
poles and their necessity for dampness or water.
And side-tracked, there was no more hope — amphibians they were and amphibians they must always remain.

But other inconspicuous chaps stuck to the safe,
middle way, and hence — we have reptiles and birds
and ourselves. The real missing links are gone forever — reptiles were too reptilian, and birds were

too avian to carry through. And after all the smugness of our ancestral line — with its slow, watchful waiting, and wading through safe and sane slime, and keeping to the unexciting, sure path marked Up and Onward or Excelsior — some of them I am sure named Eric or Bertie or Reginald — I go back to the clean, smashing waves and I see the limpets and hydroids and crabs, and I look into the bright knowing eyes of the gobies and we feel something in common. I again recall what Colonel Theodore Roosevelt said to me many years ago, " If I were the last of my race I would rather be a sabre-toothed tiger than a field mouse," and I hope in my heart I am not a typical middle-liner. There is something that transcends comfort and contentment, safety and sanity. I would rather be a goby than a salamander.

CHAPTER VI

FLOUNDERS ARE WONDERFUL

WHAT first set me thinking of flounders and phrases was a remark made when *filet de sole* came on the table.

" Here is brain food and a dainty."

Big with conceit and the smugness of a purist after many recent hours with Crabb, I gave the kind of answer which only deep friendship can withstand.

" Brain food perhaps, but not a dainty; only a delicacy."

" Well then, I suppose *filet de sole* is not sustenance! "

" Decidedly not, for you are paying for it; but I must admit it is nourishing and wholesome."

Came the reply, — " Right-ho! Rollo and Eric will now begin to dispatch their aliment, with perchance a pasty, until some ailment does them inconvenience."

I thought it better at this point to change the subject.

Months later, when a fairy flounder came up in one of my nets from the chill and blackness of a mile down, I exclaimed,

" What a miracle, this little chap! "

FLOUNDERS ARE WONDERFUL

And then I thought of the English language and I remembered that miracles are supernatural, marvels are often fictitious, while prodigies are extravagant and imaginary. Only wonders are natural. And that is in itself a most pleasant word, so I was satisfied. Flounders are wonderful: Remains only the problem to make you think so.

Competition, I suppose, is at the bottom of all flounders, soles, other flatfish and of much else in the world. Evolution does not always mean elevation, and many an advance is a progression downward. I hardly know whether to include in this category the fall of Lucifer, although he is most assuredly more human than his noble brethren of the skies, being at least a monophyletic, mammalian combination of artiodactyl, chiropterian and human, rather than an impossible homo-avian hybrid.

In the more acknowledged course of evolution man landed in the branches before he did on his feet; one out of a hundred proofs is the greater number of fallen arches among policemen than in second-story men.

Two of the three necessary objects of existence of living beings on the earth are the search for food and the avoidance of enemies. Today we find a considerable percentage of mankind avoiding an upright position in accomplishing both; millions go to their work like moles underground, and when the contested subway seats are all gone, the remaining humans support their feeble verticality by clutching leathery imitation branches. As to actual labor for food, I can recall only astronomers, mariners, steeple-jacks, rain-makers and hunters who do not sit and bend over work-bench or desk, stir up the soil or burrow into the earth itself.

As to avoiding enemies, we modern soldiers have reverted to far-distant, legless ancestors and crawl about trenches, and in and out of barbed wire and shell-holes, reserving speed and the noble upright carriage of mankind for running away.

One hundred million years ago, more or less, sharks of sorts were swimming about in oceans, twisting up, down, and around. Competition, then as now, was severe and new haunts and new sources of food were most desirable things. It was possible to stand upon one's head and feed upon delectable bottom life, but it left many openings for attack and was hard upon sensitive snouts. So to meet the situation, a zoölogy teacher in Tennessee will tell you that God suddenly made skates and rays and other flat sharks; one evolutionist will say that some sharks were slightly flatter than others, and that these kept near the bottom and married in their own set, and had children with still flatter tummies and so on until a generation appeared at which, if men had then been invented, they would have exclaimed, " Oh! skates! " Or they might have developed by mutation or emergent evolution, or by good old Darwinian action and reaction of variation, isolation, selection and environment. Relegating the Tennessee idea to the limbo of unperformed

19. Young Butterflyingfish caught with net in slick one mile from land.

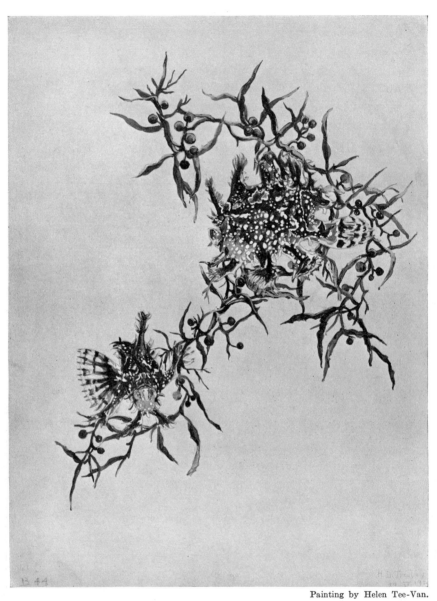

20. Sargassum Fish among its floating weed.

miracles, the others may be summed up in a crude
paraphrasing of a famous couplet:

There are nine and sixty ways in the
evolution maze
And part of every one of them is right.

Anyway, the skates and rays settled themselves
comfortably on the bottom of the sea, some time
during the Jurassic period, and developed all sorts
of new arrangements. It is not pleasant to try to
breathe water when you are lying with your face
in the mud and sand, so skates have developed a
hole or spiracle on the upper side of their head,
which they can open at will and draw water through,
instead of through the mouth; and they have not
only flattened, but spread out sideways into thin
wings, with which they flap, bird-like, on their way
through life.

Fifty million years passed, and then, just as in
the movies, came a day when the ancestors of all
flounders became dissatisfied with their place in the
world. The mid-water pickings were not what they
used to be before the influx of all the modern fish,
and the oldest sole could remember the time when —
but then came an urge, " Go down, young sole, go
down." And the young soles and flounders, which
were then just ordinary fish, swam down. They were
rather deep-keeled, not round and tubby like the
early sharks, and they peered down around themselves like a fat man trying to see if his shoe-lace is
untied. And they saw the skates and rays having

a grand time all to themselves on the ocean floor, but all their own efforts to press down merely hurt their spines and got them nowhere.

The urge was insistent, however, and they never gave up. When tired out they would probably sink down and wearily lie over on one side for a time, and their attempts at snatching food below the belt resulted in a constant careening of the whole body. In one, or in nine, or in nine and sixty ways they persisted and finally they succeeded.

If I watch very carefully and walk exceedingly slowly over the sand of Almost Island I believe I can safely count on a fresh marvel every fathom of distance (we must be ultra-submarine in our language). Sometimes the adventure is so inexplicable that I choose temporarily to call it a miracle — a small one perhaps, like that invoked by Chubu and Sheamish — but a miracle until my reluctant recollection of schismatic facts of physics and zoölogy demand the rejection of this, and the substitution, as before, of wonder.

On the last but one of my dives the sun was shining full strength and the shadow of my feet as I walked six fathoms deep loomed large and black on the sand. At my third step, like the charwoman's active shadow in the house of magic, a shade slipped away from beneath my feet, just before the substance would have met and destroyed it. Up and up it floated and I froze still and watched. As it rose it gained in substantialness and when near my eyes was marked with a harmonious blending of gray

and buffy-brown, with a scattered handful of turquoise circles and crescents, these becoming more
and more distinct with every foot of altitude.

Only one metaphor was possible when I viewed
the peacock flounder in its own element from one
side close up as man to fish, — a flying carpet. The
design was that of some old Persian born of generations of feeling for color and pattern, woven with
a skill which only love of the work could initiate and
sustain, and finally leavened with the bloom of time
and usage. Even so, the aquatic tapestry was incom-
parable, for as I watched it turn and return in mid-
water, it changed tint and altered pattern in full
course, darkening as a cloud shadow passed, clearing with the return of the sun. When it banked,
the pure white underside flashed out like snow on
grass. It swam past once more, and the surrounding
aura of parti-colored fins waved like the most delicate of fringe — its motive power combining amazing efficiency of control with exceeding beauty of
pigment and grace of movement. Down each side
flowed an endless series of undulations, an adum-
bration far beneath the sea of what water is able
to achieve only in contact with air.

As I watched, I seemed to detect a continual dis-
play of energy on the part of the crew of this flying
carpet. Just forward of amidships was a mast and
a sail, — an exceedingly active sail, which was being continually but slowly raised and lowered. It
was astonishing to see the mast stepped into place,
and then an unbelievably exact lateen sail, unfurled

and spread taut. It had a series of yards or slats like the sails I have seen on Chinese junks. A little forward of this was the bridge, or conning towers, — call them what you will, always remembering that the corresponding human structures have been in use a scant three decades. In comparison with the first invention of flounders' controls, this would be about one minute of time to two years.

Periscope is perhaps the most apposite comparison, for these were the eyes of the peacock flounder, — two tall, cylindrical elevations which turned and twisted freely in their sockets, one cocked up aloft at me as the fish swam past, or quite independently revolving to cover all points of possible danger. As the volant raft banked sharply I again caught a glimpse of the whitewashed hull, and in the center of this I perceived a keel, — a deep, abrupt one such as is carried by great racing yachts. This was not leadenly quiescent but constantly shifted according to requirements, operating quite independently of the mast and sail on the top deck.

All this and more I had seen, when the flounder spiralled up to a level with my helmet, then turned and with fin-turbines motionless, sail filled and quiet, it glided smoothly down, volplaning at an even, gentle angle, banking very slightly inward. As it passed my eyes it was as dark as a water-diluted shadow should be, with the blue ornaments barely visible. I watched it curve down out of view behind me, and some instinct impelled me to relax my stiffened limbs and sink slowly to my knees. I

21. The gorge through which I fought my way to sea.

22. On calm days the tidepools of Nonsuch can be explored for rare fish.

waited hopefully but nothing happened, and I feared my fish had gone forever. Bending my head as far back as I dared I caught sight of my own stream of breath bubbles and through the mass of silvery — can I call them drops of air — swam the oval flounder, looking from beneath as white as the bubbles themselves. I could not long hold my position and twisted back, and within three seconds the fish appeared directly in front, and came to the gentlest of landings before my eyes.

Even if I had been in the upper air where ears are ears, and armed with a microphone, I doubt if it would have recorded the grating of one sand grain upon another — with such infinite softness did the flying carpet at last come to rest. When within an inch or two of the ocean's floor, with sail and fringe-like oars it put on silent brakes, lost impetus and, as a shadow halts, it settled in a little over its own length. Simultaneously the dark cloak — the dusky pattern deserving of some mysterious Persian room, close latticed against the sun — in the twinkling of an eye was absorbed into thin water, and replaced by a fairy-like tan and white lacery; and that went, and there was in its place nothing but sand, and the flounder had become a figment of my imagination — it was as if it never had been. The mast, sail and periscopes had been stowed, the fringe was gone — I was looking not at a peacock flounder, not at an eight-inch *Platophrys lunatus,* but at a smooth extent of sand.

One of the exciting things about the development

and evolution of a flounder — exciting because we
can offer no reason for it — is that although this
bottom adaptation has been going on steadily without a break for fifty million years, it seems to come
to every baby flounder as a new idea — a thought
which has just occurred to him. He shows no hint
of not growing into a normal upright fish, until
suddenly all of him begins at once. And before this
there is a bit of prophetic internal anatomy which
foreshadows the change; a bar of cartilage over one
eye is absorbed after being carefully laid down.
It reminds me of galloping policemen or a motor-
cycle squad which speeds down an avenue clearing
it for the passage of some important personage.
The cartilage bar out of the way, the path is clear
for the transformation.

After a few weeks of life, feeding on minute
swimming animals, the young flounder or sole begins to sag to one side, toward the right usually,
and now ensues the amazing thing that every tissue
and organ in the body begins to twist — bones,
nerves, muscles, everything. And as the little creature lies more and more flat, an astronomical
miracle (no other word fits it) occurs in its little
cosmos, a second great sun rises over the rim of its
new horizon — the right eye has left its habitual
bed and climbed aloft, aided by muscles and even
bones, and within a week's time has come to rest
close beside the other eye. The mouth twists slowly
day by day, until the fish has assumed a curious
wistful expression, and what is more to the point

is ready to change diet to bottom creatures, or to leap up and seize passing fish.

Instead of the paired fins growing into waving wings as in the flattened shark, the vertical fins increase, growing forward to the very snout and back to the tail fin, thus forming a circle of fin about the fish. The right pectoral remains small and functions as a keel, while, as we have seen in the peacock flounder, the left pectoral grows almost as long as the body, and can scull and sail right lustily.

Flatfish are far from being sedentary even if they do look at life from a cross-eyed bottom point of view. One fish, marked and set at liberty, averaged more than a quarter of a mile a day for over two years before it was captured again. The dangers which beset these little individualists are legion and are reflected in the number of eggs laid, which may reach twelve or fourteen million. Yet in spite of the enemies whose whole diet consists of filet of sole on the fin, enormous numbers survive — unquestionable proof of the value of a life spent prone on the bottom.

From the time of the Egyptians, flatfish and especially soles have been considered great delicacies; poetry has been composed in their honor and they have been painted and hewn in stone. My adventure with the peacock flounder recalls the old Greek myth concerning soles, that these foot-shaped flatfish were worn by regal water nymphs:

103

NONSUCH

> " And next (the goddesses such sandals wear)
> Of mighty soles, a firm and well-matched pair."

Radcliffe recounts a tale of South Sea mythology, a sort of Just So story of the flatfish. " Ina the daughter of Vaitooringa attempted flight to the sacred island. Fish after fish essayed to bear her thither, but unequal to the burden, dropped her in the shallow water. At last she besought the sole, who managed to carry her as far as the breakers. Here, again unshipped, she lost her divine temper, and stamped with such fierceness on the head of the unfortunate helper of distressful maids that its under eye was squeezed right through to the upper side. Hence the sole is now obliged to swim flat on one side of its face, having no eye on the lower side."

In mid-May I captured an eight-inch peacock flounder so close to Almost Island that it may have been my first flying carpet. I kept it for many weeks in an ill-aerated aquarium whose occasional lack of oxygen killed all the other inmates, but seemed to cause no inconvenience to the flounder.

One early morning I crept quietly toward the fish and found it flat as any creature could be and yet live. The bottom of the aquarium had only the thinnest skim of sand, yet all that was visible was a thickening of this sand near the center: One could not say here the sand ended and there the fish began. I made a sudden movement, and then I saw a slight shift of the grains and realized I was being closely watched by a bright eye through a slit of imitation

sand. Jason could not have been more surprised at
his reaping than I, when everything on board the
flounder began working at once. I am sure the right
kind of microphone could have registered a faint
four bells.

Slowly the encircling rays near the head of the
fish began pushing and straightening, until they
were nearly upright, bending under the weight, but
holding their owner high above the bottom. Simultaneously the mast and attendant yards were lifted,
three rays of the pectoral fin waving on high the full
length of the body. Without clank of machinery or
whisper of orders, the two turreted eyes rose from
far forward, and the peacock flounder was cleared
for action.

The eyes were so uncanny I watched them for
half an hour. The sides of the turrets were conspicuous, a clear buffy-brown, for these were usually
concealed. The flat summits were at present iridescent — green, blue and yellow, but could be flooded
with pure arenaceous at an instant's notice. From
the outer rim of the top there floated out behind two
rather stiffish, fleshy tentacles, with a few lesser filaments hanging from them. These gave a most
jaunty air, a cockatoo-crest of sorts, which, sprouting from a turret, leaves us in a sad welter of mixed
metaphors.

Unlike the exposed part of the eye of most fishes,
that of the peacock flounder was not round, but con-
stricted by encroaching skin to a broad horizontal
crescent. This resulted from a rounded flap which

hung down over the upper part of the pupil. After I looked for a long time I saw why this was — the eye was no longer an eye but an irregular pebble or sand grain, and as I watched I saw the crescent become a narrow slit, then a cross section of the third of a circle, and back again to crescent.

The flounder winked, withdrawing one eye-turret and moving it slowly about between decks, then up again. Twice something happened straight overhead which I could not detect, and first one, then both eyes rolled upward. Later they made a careful horizontal reconnaissance of the visible world, each turning in more than a half circle, and between them completely boxing the compass.

With a hand lens I slowly brought the restless eyes into focus through the side of the aquarium, and soon I felt a distinct embarrassment. In no other fish and in few mammals have I ever felt such intelligence and understanding of itself, its environment and myself as these amazing eyes seemed to convey. Both swung around and gazed steadily, unblinkingly at me, slight up and down movements indicating (to my imagination at least) an acute appraising of my features and gauging of my intentions. A fish flashed in the next aquarium, and both eyes turned swiftly, the farther to hold steady on the new interest, the other turning back immediately to complete its estimate of my temper and my purposes. Nothing could have made me injure the peacock flounder after that. By luck and accident I had netted and confined a fish, but eye to eye I saw his spirit was tranquil, his confidence undisturbed, he awaited my next move with alertness, but without worry.

My hand lens had restricted my view to the eyes and their immediate vicinity and when my protesting muscles compelled me to lower the lens my mind received another shock. I had so long and intensively been preoccupied with the seeming intelligence of these sophisticated eyes that I had forgotten the rest of the owner. Unconsciously I looked for concomitant features and head.

Imagine gazing into two expressive human eyes, in which you seem to read character, sympathy and all splendid human attributes, and then suddenly to take a wider view and see to your horror that the eyes are protuding from the cheek and temple of the distorted face. This is not such an absurd metaphor, for I experienced something of the same thing when I saw anew the twisted mouth and the outrageous position of the flounder's eyes. Back I went to my lens, and my mind re-insisted that I was looking at the eyes of some friendly, normal fellow creature which for some reason was perched upon the back of this prostrate flounder.

One more surprise was in store for me. When I had had the flounder for a week, he had been for some time the sole survivor of the tank. I then captured a three-inch wrasse and dropped him in. For some reason I stayed and watched the wrasse swim leisurely about near the surface. The flounder also saw the new-comer and both eyes were brought to bear. It then left the bottom and slowly undulated upward. When still some distance away, its mouth opened wider than in normal breathing, in a gasp of sorts, and when I turned and looked for the wrasse it had vanished — I was about to add, with more of a truism than a simile — as if swallowed up.

My eye had recorded not even a flicker; the wrasse had made no struggle or effort. One moment it had been swimming and the next it was not there. I tried two more wrasse, with identical results except that by watching unwinkingly I was able to see a confused quiver in the water between wrasse and flounder. But it in no way accounted to my brain for what must have happened; my human eyesight was geared too low. The feat was possible only by a sudden, tremendously powerful current of water sucked in through the mouth and out at the gills, engulfing the helpless wrasse headlong in the oral maelstrom.

Finally I tried a small puffer and for once my peacock flounder was baffled. Though with lightning swiftness the watery vortex surged past, the little chap's inflating machinery worked still more rapidly, and this time the gastronomic sleight-of-hand ended in the flounder's ejecting a half-circular, unswallowable, completely self-possessed, small, prickly puffer.

I had watched a flying carpet bank in spirals about me, six and thirty feet beneath the surface; I had seen sheer magic worked in my aquarium; I had looked into eyes which somehow deserved

Photograph by Mr. Hamilton.

23. A truce is declared at low tide on the Battlefield of the Shore.

24. The plants of the sea (upper) and of the land (lower) almost meet at the tidepool's edge.

my anthropomorphic flattery. The next time I look down at my *filet de sole,* I will say to my companion:

" I was wrong. It is not only a dainty, it is wonderful, and the best brain food I have ever known."

CHAPTER VII

TO write honestly and with conviction anything
about the migration of birds, one should oneself have migrated.

But not every millionaire who in the autumn goes
in his private car to Palm Beach and returns in the
spring can claim fellow feeling with the migrant
birds, although there is a firm basis of communion.
A single night in a lighthouse or in the torch of the
Statue of Liberty might conceivably be a better
preparation. But somehow or other we must dehu-
manize ourselves, feel the feel of feathers on our
body, and the wind in our wings, and finally know
what it is to leave luxury and safety, and yield to
the compelling instinct, age-old, at the moment
seemingly quite devoid of reason and object.

In any case the chief pleasure either in thinking
or writing is pragmatic. The more I can sink my six
feet to the stature of an ant, the more right have I
to attempt to interpret an ant's feelings and emotions; if I can feel scaly instead of skinny, can know
a wave and a coral reef intimately from beneath
as well as above, so much better may I hope to sense
the joys and sorrows of any poor fish.

I have been lost alone in an airplane at night, I

110

have swung so low that birds were frightened from
their roosts in the tree-tops; a glow now and then
through the fog ceiling made it seem as if I were
contour flying blindly; I have swung around and
around a cluster of lights peering vainly for hint of
a landing place. Finally, in deadly fear, I have
climbed to temporary safety, gambled the low tide
in my fuel tanks against the dawn, and won by a
glimmer. Only because of this do I feel worthy of
writing something about the migration of birds.

The real dramatic phase of migration is the ultimate object, enhanced by the fact that earthly creatures become helpless pawns when once this fateful
hysteria claims them. With many living beings migration operates as a saver of life; to legions of
others it is a forced march to certain death.

When a hawk or wild goose passes overhead, my
pet monkey, Chiriqui, ducks in fear or dives into his
house. A migrant bird is to him merely a stimulus to
inherited memory of the deadly swoop of harpy
eagles. To our n^{th} great-granduncles — the cave-
men — the coming of swallows must have meant no
more than buzzing flies — possibly not so much. In
historical times I seem to associate the first conscious thought of migrating birds with astrologers
and the absence of sloping roofs. From the earliest
times in the Far East men liked to sleep or to study
the stars on the flat tops of their houses, and many
an abstruse calculation of star portents of war or
prophets must have been interrupted by the loud
chirps of passing birds. Even this I have verified

111

for myself, for many years ago I evaded a pair of sleepy guards and climbed by night to the apex of Cheops. There I stretched out and pretended I was an astrologer vizier of some Pharaoh of olden time. And I remember sitting up so quickly that I nearly fell down one of the giant steps, when a low *'tsip! 'tsip!* came to my ears. It was the slightest whisper of a sound but it destroyed Egypt and my viziership, and replaced them with a more prosaic landscape and personality, recalling the time when, on a distant continent, as a boy, I listened each spring and autumn to the chirps of the migrating hosts.

One fortunate night I was permitted a glimpse of these vast flocks. I squatted on the swaying floor of the torch of the Statue of Liberty when the fog drifted in from the sea and closed down grey and silent. With it came birds which before had been only disembodied voices, and the fog, which obliterated the heavens and the earth, made the migrating flocks visible to my eyes. More and more they came, until a swarm of golden bees was the only simile I could think of. I dared not face them full, for now and then one struck the light with terrific impact. So I peered from behind the railing and watched the living atoms dash into view, shine for an instant, and vanish, so rapidly that when I looked through half-closed lids the driving sparks consolidated and lengthened into luminous lines. I think that I enjoyed it as a spectacle more in retrospect than at the time, for my emotion was distracted by the occasional thud at my feet of black-

112

25. The passive resistance of the Sea Anemone enables it to live and thrive in the zone of crashing breakers.

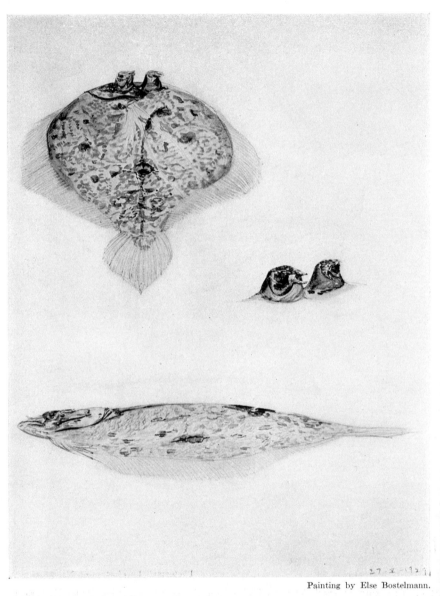

Painting by Else Bostelmann.

26. The periscope eyes of the Peacock Flounder.

polls and other warblers. It seemed such a cruel thing that even one of these lives which had been hatched and fed with such care in Hudson Bay or Labrador should be needlessly snuffed out because of the glare through a bit of glass.

Tens of thousands of facts have been gathered and collated concerning the migration of birds, but as to origins and causes we can only surmise and imagine.

To clarify the subject of migration I need to divorce it from the mere organism which manifests it — to emphasize the obsession, the absolute obligation to go and go, apart from the specific swallow or duck, lemming or butterfly which temporarily houses this mysterious daemon. I shall try to do this by continuing the simile of the swarm of golden bees about the lighthouse, and let a golden glow typify the migration instinct.

Even human history sheds a little light on our subject. Hannibal forged a tiny flicker of migratory flame over the Alps, the glow of which slowly died down in the plains of farther Italy. Attila and his following hordes were agleam with it when wave after wave of them broke against the Roman legions, finally to be smothered by the Eternal City itself. It is distressing to think what our blood and mental equipment would be today had not our piratical ancestors — the winged hats — executed the most lasting migrations known to humans. A very cool, white flame burned in the Mayflower, and even today, our aforementioned Goddess of Liberty watches, perhaps a little humorously, faint sparks within the shawl-wrapped forms of the steerage, floating past, upstream, toward migration's melting-pot.

But these are all trifling migrations, whims of empire, tribe or family, variously origined and of brief duration. We must go to the so-called lower animals to find migration in all the majesty of age-old tradition, its beginnings buried in past geological epochs, with routes fashioned by long forgotten configurations of continents, ancient before mankind had risen up on his hind legs or climbed into the trees — migrations whose times and seasons have been evolved and governed by countless centuries of revolutions of the planet earth.

From a lofty vantage point let us watch the coast lines of Labrador and Greenland and as far north as any frozen bit of earth distinguishes itself from sheer ice. It is July and the breathlessly short Arctic summer is at its height. As an icicle loses a few drops between clouds, so this northland relaxes its grip for a brief season, countable in days, and permits a few inches of thaw and of dwarfed and hasty growth of moss and flowers to slip through its icy fingers. All is grey and white — sea, old snowdrifts and birds. The birds have come, like the intermittent drops from the icicle, settling to earth from nowhere at the first hint of thaw, scratching a shallow hollow, and brooding four huddled eggs. The breast of the mother tern is a tiny oasis of warmth amid the Arctic waste; her food is inchling

114

fish snatched at brief intervals from the edge of the ice. She stakes the hatching and the feeding of the young against the swift passing of the midnight sun, and scarcely is the brood awing before the meagre foliage blackens, the soil turns to iron, and the last ripple freezes over. She has won, but only by a margin of hours.

All along the Arctic shores from Labrador to within a few hundred miles of the pole, we from aloft now discern a faint glow — our imagined glow of the birth of the instinct of migration. It increases, and soon the restlessness of the birds is changed to impatience, and impatience to complete surrender and these bits of northernmost life beat southward across the face of the planet. There are thousands upon thousands of them. They have ceased to be every-Arctic-Tern-in-the-world, they are not *Sterna paradisaea,* they are no longer parents or young or this or that individual, but a unified cohort of organisms set apart, obsessed, glowing at fever heat with the thralldom of migration.

In the face of unknowable mystery I often imagine myself the Creator, or, as in this case, the Instigator of Instinct, and plan out what seems wisest and best. This exercise frequently shows me why the obvious is seldom probable. In regard to these migrants I should without hesitation lead them to Bermuda. Here, as I shall repeat elsewhere in this volume, is a compact swarm of islands with an infinity of rocky crags and caves and beaches fit for safe perching and sleeping; here are multitudes of delectable fry of just the right size; here are man-made laws ensuring safety from molestation. Here also (although the least important of all natural reasons) are thousands of human eyes ready to see and admire, perhaps many human beings who would be the better for having their thoughts diverted, by the sight of beauty, from the humor engendered by an ill lead at bridge or an irritating drive on the golf course.

Yet not a single migrant of this species veers eastward to these desirable isles. They hold steadfast to the south. They must sleep and eat, but, steady as the feather-end of the compass arrow, they swing on and on, covering only a little less than two hundred miles each day. If storms hold them back, they make up time, with ever warmer and warmer air whistling through their wings. Around Cape Cod, past Cape Hatteras, along Florida beaches — the hot sun of the tropics replacing the cold, blue shine of the Greenland midnight; threading the West Indies, skirting Brazilian jungles, and diving for strange fish off the shores of the Argentine. The sun swings lower, the last breath of warmth is strained from the air, as Patagonia and Magellen's Straits vanish below the horizon. After eleven thousand miles have passed behind, the birds sight the gigantic ice barrier of the Antarctic, and here the migration glow dies down and expires. Here they sleep and preen their plumage, catching fish in company with penguins instead of polar bears, their grey and white feathers illumined by the sun for all the duration of their stay.

Four months pass. The ice is just as cold, the air as bitter, there is no change in the character or abundance of food, yet again comes the restlessness, and northward goes every bird, reflying the eleven thousand miles of whirling globe, and redistributing themselves. If the gods of little birds have been kind to any single pair, the chances are they will meet and mate again, and deposit their eggs in the selfsame hollow.

These are the facts. But what about Why? One recent answer is that " annual migration cannot be looked upon as an act of volition, but as the automatic response to a certain physiological state probably induced by a gonadial hormone." And this, in spite of itself, is very probably true, and contains a core of dramatic interest equal only to the more perspicuous phase of the subject with which we are at present concerned. It is clear that our Arctic terns must move south from their breeding grounds or be starved and frozen to death. But now that we know that they crave ice and stress of storm and small fish in frigid seas, why should they go farther south than Labrador? It would seem that this obsession of migration sometimes acquires such an impetus that only the whole long length of the planet itself can dissipate it.

If we find mystery in the migration of the Arctic tern we are still less able to explain the annual movements of many other birds. Of those which are not forced to move by oncoming frost, some are content to shift a few miles southward, others to cross mountain ranges and wide stretches of open ocean, to winter in unfamiliar torrid jungles. If our fancied glow of the instinct was a reality, our spring and autumn nights would show an unending blaze of avian meteors which would dim the moon and stars. After exhausting our explanations of the means of guidance, such as landmarks, sea currents, winds, stars and a magnetic sense, we must, in some instances at least, fall back on an inexplicable sense of direction. And when we have taken refuge in this pleasantly all-comprehensive phrase, we remember those species in which the young migrate before their parents — and rather willingly change the subject.

At least we have moderated our ideas as to altitude and speed. Instead of a height of three miles above the earth, we know from airplane and other observations, that nocturnal migrants seldom average more than a half mile height. In the daytime, however, flocks of storks, geese and plover have been seen two miles up going full speed. The record is perhaps several geese in the western Himalayas photographed at an estimated height equal to that of Mount Everest.

Until stop-watches and airplanes gave us definite data we were willing to accept with wondering credulity a speed of two hundred and forty miles an hour attributed to many birds. The cruel exactitude of definite observation has brought this down

MIGRATION

to forty miles an hour for crows and sixty for ducks.
Swifts unquestionably hold the record with one hundred and very rarely one hundred and fifty miles an hour, this during their aerial feeding, not on migration.

During the two annual seasons, few vessels pass through the major lines of migration flight without affording temporary sanctuary to birds in distress. This is only a hint of the terrible dangers and toll of mortality demanded by migration. Year after year the same number of house wrens return to our orchards, sing from our tree-tops and rear their broods in our knot-holes. If fortune is kind, a single pair of wrens may rear twenty young in a season. So in October two and twenty feathered mites take to the air some night and go to the Gulf Coast or beyond. The following spring one or both parents often return to the same nesting hollow, and as last year, a second pair is singing in the orchard. But no others are within our range. Ninety per cent — twenty out of twenty-two wrens — have perished, their little bodies devoured by hawk or owl, dashed against the glass of lighthouses, or drowned in the spray of the open ocean. Now and then a house wren spends the entire winter in the north, finding sufficient shelter and food, and yet his fellows go hundreds of miles beyond the latitude of warmth and abundance of insects, obeying some long-lost law of past initiation of this compelling instinct.

Migration in other fields presents us with infinitely greater tragedies. Every wren has at least

119

a hope, a fighting chance of returning to its birth-place, but not so the hordes of butterflies and lemmings. I have stood on the shore of the sea and watched thousands upon hundreds of thousands of yellow butterflies fluttering by, appearing endlessly over the top of the jungle, drifting like volant autumn leaves down river courses, and without an instant of hesitation, passing out over the line of breakers, beyond the emerald shallows, to disappear on the horizon between sky and deep sea — not one ever to return. The puzzle is no nearer to solution when we capture one, a dozen, a thousand, and find them all males; not a single female butterfly among all the mad host of suicides.

A small colony of lemmings — those little furry rodents of Scandinavia — is the most static community imaginable. The little chaps hop in and out of their burrows, and alternately sleep the hours away or nibble eternally at grass blades. Now and then a litter of four or five young appears. After several years of apparently uneventful, idyllic life, even during a cold or rainy year, the younger generations apparently refuse to die from the usual natural causes. They breed sooner than is the custom, after a few months of life, and the litters increase to nine or ten. The warren swarms with lemmings of all ages, and whole generations — especially of the young males — begin to push down the mountain slopes and river valleys.

At first the extension is gradual and is slowed up or stopped when areas of rich pasture are reached.

But a strange impetus then possesses them, and in the dark (if we may be permitted to continue our simile) we would see the fields and woods aglow with the swiftly accumulating instinct. The passion of migration descends upon them, and in solid phalanxes, in crowded mats and roads of life the lemming host sets forth. All appetite is left behind, and while on the march the most succulent food is passed by. On and on they go, fording rivers, trampling crops, regardless of the owls, weasels, hawks and foxes harrying their flanks, paying no attention to the guns and clubs of the men whom they encounter. Thousands of them live to reach the outermost beach, and like the tropical butterflies, they press on, fighting their way through the surf, thrown back in windrows of drowned. Ferocious fish replace their enemies of the air and land, until, swimming on and on, the last pitiful gasp is given far from land, and the ultimate lemming sinks slowly through the water of the open sea. Another lemming migration is over.

I think the most spectacular migration in the world, combining the characters of those of the Arctic tern and the lemming, is the single great journey of the common eel. After a decade or more spent in some inland lake or far up near the headwaters of a river, all the adult eels of the same age descend to the ocean — eels of the Hudson, Potomac, St. Lawrence, Elbe, Rhine, Loire — all seek the Atlantic and traverse many hundreds of miles of its waters to the southwest part of the Sargasso

NONSUCH

Sea, and there lay their eggs and die. In the course
of time, the young eels return — how, we have no
slightest idea — to the respective continents and
rivers from which their parents came, and the
miracle is complete.

Year by year the breeding ranges of all the creatures in the world become more limited. No week
passes but sees the complete wiping out of some
bird or beast or insect. The way of the bird in the
air is ever more perilous as the beacons and lights
of humanity increase. The winter homes are being
rendered barren by vast rubber plantations and
other man-fashioned what-nots. Throughout a few
more decades only will the old migrations still hold.
For no matter how simple and easy the shortening
or rerouting of a flight might be, the last surviving
bird in which glows the spark of this possessing instinct will endure the new dangers, will strive to
overcome the appalling handicaps thrown across its
path. The method and completion of an instinct
originating before man came to know he was himself can never be altered or turned aside in the few
brief years of his dominance. Only the death of the
last bird or animal or insect can achieve that.

CHAPTER VIII

WHEN you look for things and hope for things and greatly desire things year after year, and train your senses to continue their concentration after the less important parts of you are sleeping or eating or playing or merely talking, then sooner or later, very special things happen within sight or hearing, smell or touch, radius. I have been lucky, for a queen termite once began her miraculous city at the very moment I was crossing my compound; giant fruit-bats have crossed the surface of the moon just as I focused glasses on it; a Sclater's impeyan pheasant reached the summit of a bamboo hill in northern Burma as I crept up the opposite slope; shooting stars seem often to hang back in obscurity until I am looking at their exact future path, and I have missed more than one important lob at tennis because a rare migrant drew my eye to the sky beyond.

For two days a single greater yellow-legs had lived on South Beach, Nonsuch, feeding, sleeping and chumming with a band of turnstones and benefiting by their football rushes against the loose clumps of stranded sargassum. The third day, August 9th, 1931, most of me was deep in the char-

123

acters of a new species of *Pseudoscopelus* when suddenly my ears, which were wholly bored with this microscopic work, pulled all the rest of me out of my chair and rushed me outdoors. My focusing hands, my squinting eyes, my technical convolutions had no chance against the sudden aural demand — the call of a passing sandpiper being the electric spark of a sound which had sprung the mine.

Back and forth overhead swung my yellow-legs, calling as he went — then seaward. My hands needed no help in unleashing and orienting my large glasses, my eyes knew better than to leave this ventriloquial note in the wide heavens. Down along the top of the barrels I followed him, and almost without a break sighted him again, grown twelve times larger, in the lenses. I had a comfortable ledge on which to rest and swivel the glasses. Five hundred feet above the sea he encountered a stiff breeze and for many minutes fought and fought against it. My heart ached, for he was headed due south and I knew that no land this side of Cuba or Haiti would give him rest, and yet here he was using up vitality and strength battling a wall of wind only a few hundred yards off Nonsuch. Suddenly he seemed to give up, and swung around and back in a great circle almost overhead, then the frantic pressing forward began again. If the bird had been the negative end of a compass needle, the austral pull could not have been more continuous.

Three times he circled and three times lost all he had gained, and then, as so often in my life, I realized that my pity was needless, my sympathy was engendered only by my human conceit, for my eyes suddenly sensed that from the moment I first saw the bird he had been gaining altitude — at first so gradually that my brain refused to record the diminution — and now more swiftly. I did not dare to wink; now and then I confused the brave sandpiper with some mote in my eye's circulation, but before he passed wholly and forever beyond my view I saw the last spiral straighten out, and with elemental directness, high above the stratum of head wind, he sped straight out to sea, with a strength and assurance which streamed through the last thin column of vision between the beating wings of the bird and my eye. My straining eyes compelled a wink, and there was left in my glasses only a round view of blue sky with a cottony cloud in the lower left-hand corner.

As I walked back to my laboratory table and my neglected *Pseudoscopelus,* my ears again demanded attention, not for present audibility but for what they had been recording while I was just one large eye. Only now I realized that one of the most astonishing things about the whole occurrence was the penetrating clarity with which the sweet, high call of the bird had continued — *wheu — wheu — wheu — wheu!* I thought back and a cunning self-recording part of my brain intimately connected with the switchboard of my ears, told me accurately that I had heard the voice of the yellow-legs until the second spiral — a spiral which, in my ignorance, I had called a circle. I checked up another very special event which made life on Earth supremely satisfying; I thanked my subconscious ears very heartily. They saluted, looked rather superiorly at my *Pseudoscopelus,* and went back to their listening post.

Now and then, looking southward from Nonsuch, we see incoming steamers headed our way, passing along close beyond the outer reefs. The telescope shows strange flags, alien names, and sometimes, when it is very clear, foreign folk peering over the rails. The next day we see in St. Georges swarthy South American faces and listen to liquid, neo-tropical, Latin exclamations. Another day and all are gone again.

Early in my occupancy of Nonsuch I wandered down to South Beach. Out among the stranded sargassum weed I saw a movement and a second glance showed a trim little figure running among the piled fronds, now and then hesitating to snatch at some morsel, but forever teetering. My glasses revealed an old friend in a new dress — a spotless spotted sandpiper. His breast was swept clear of all pattern, his winter waistcoat was immaculate. And the next day, like the migrant South Americans from the ships, he too was gone.

The job I had set myself on my new island home was the study of the fish of the deep sea and the shore, but I would choose any day to be a poor naturalist than a good ultra-specialist. So forthwith, looking ahead to other migrant birds, I built me a blind of driftwood and boxes at the hither end of the beach, between two low cedars, where I had a clear view of the shrubs, grass, sand and water which composed the hundred yards of the crescent cove.

And by the way, when age forecloses my life mortgage of activity, and I can only hobble, I shall use up a year to good advantage near a beach like this — studying and recording the amazing changes, day by day, in physical geography, in its wracks and wrecks, its seaweed, shells, jellyfish, the storm-driven pieces of broken boats, and things dropped overboard — all so beloved of Jabim: And far from least, the migrant birds which come, and feed, and rest, and go.

My blind which, when finished, looked uncomfortably like a front trench dug-out, was my Mecca for a short time early every morning. I found that just before sun-up gave the best visibility. I began with Zeiss Number 3's, then 6's and finally swept the beach with Number 12's, only the last had to be rested on the topmost box and swivelled like a machine-gun. Each glass spoiled me for the preceding, and one day I completed my optical downfall, and laid up bad trouble ahead. I see in the future, times of muscle agony, of weary, overladen tramps through swamps, through bitter cold, through blistering heat; scores of times of physical exhaustion but mental and emotional ecstasy. All because I was tempted to lug my giant telescope-

binoculars down to the beach. They are brob-
dignagian opera-glasses, mighty double-barrels,
weighing 16 pounds, each tube 22 inches long, and
with revolving eye-pieces of 12, 20 and 40 diameters.

I set them up on the tripod, arranged a comfortable seat and focused. For two score years I
have been peering at wild birds through glasses of
one kind or another, but one glance now and I
realized that I had never yet really seen a wild bird.
The 12-power eye-piece gave me the same magni-
fication as my largest field-glasses, which as I have
said, are too powerful to use satisfactorily without
a rest. But here the illumination was almost of the
naked eye in full sunlight. Then I turned the 20-
power into alignment and it is a wonder that
my exclamation did not clear the beach of bird
life.

The naked eye saw a confused group too far
away for certain identification; the Number 3's permitted recognition of all but the smaller sandpipers,
but through the twin telescopes the field was completely filled by a quartet of turnstones, a sanderling
and two semipalmated sandpipers. Never satisfied,
I turned on the 40 diameters but could not get a
clear focus — I was too close! After all, this was a
telescope, not a hand lens.

I found that from my laboratory porch on Nonsuch I could focus on Castle Island, which was over
1300 yards, or three-quarters of a mile away, and
with a favorable light I could readily distinguish
between the sexes of house sparrows and even of

Photograph by Mr. Hamilton and the late Captain Neltnes.

27. Nonsuch Island from the air. The laboratories are visible, and the coral reefs from one to five fathoms deep.

28. Wading birds on migration.

bluebirds. On Brangman's, a quarter of a mile off, I could detect the most delicate coloring of bills, feet and eyes, and could identify any species of Bermuda butterfly.

With or without my telescope I kept South Beach under observation for six migration seasons — three north and three southward. This beach is the only one hereabouts which is sheltered and yet faces the open ocean. It receives more sargassum weed than any other, and this indirectly brings the migrants, for the weed offers shelter and nursery facilities to the little *Orchestia* or sand-hoppers, which, on Nonsuch, run the sun a close second as the source of life.

In the course of three years I have observed seventeen species of shore birds, all migrants, on South Beach. Seven of these I saw only once or twice — phalaropes, dowitchers, yellow-legs, willets, Hudsonian Curlews, and black-bellied and golden plovers.

Nine birds were seen frequently enough to be called regular annual visitors. Six of these were sandpipers, least, semipalmated, sanderlings, greater yellow-legs, solitary and spotted; two were plovers, semipalmated and piping, and the most abundant were the turnstones.

At first, to make sure of certain identifications, I shot a few birds, until there was no question of easy recognition at sight, and on days when no rare species appeared I studied the regulars as species personalities. All the birds I shot I found to be

NONSUCH

stuffed with the sand-hopping amphipods which lived in the seaweed, but the thing that interested me most was the inorganic contents of the small gizzards. One could always become emotional when a tired migrant swung into view and landed on the beach: One thought how the fluff of feathers had fought wind and darkness and the ever-present danger of the imminent waves for hundreds of miles from the last take-off to this speck of land in mid-Atlantic. But when I tumbled the grit from the gizzards out upon my microscope stage and focused upon it, and turned over the little particles with my finger, I had made much more than a theoretical contact with the arctic homes of these birds. In the turnstones and the least and semipalmated sandpipers, mingled with the remains of the crustaceans I found tiny bits of stone — fair rocks and boulders they looked under the lens; not the ground-up shell and sand grains and comminuted armor of crab and snail which compose the strand of Bermuda, but rounded bits of granite and glassy quartz, and red, pitted, hematite-like minerals, and here and there, a bit rough and black like lava. From Melville Bay, northern Labrador, the Yukon's mouth these came — and the scant six inches of least sandpiper brought his from Ungava, Yakutat Bay, Keewatin and perhaps the farthest point of northwestern Alaska — four thousand miles and more away. Here in my mid-Atlantic laboratory I was fingering the very soil itself from these magic lands of the north, brought to me in the bodies of the

130

shore birds. Once getting the full joy of this, I shot no more birds during my whole stay. There was no need — my telescope brought them all out of the conventional bush and placed them in my hand.

The moment we take to ourselves a bird as a pet, it becomes an individual and acquires a personality, and only one who has had to do with the building of a zoo can possibly appreciate the vast mental and emotional gulfs separating two feathered creatures which, to the eye, are absolutely identical.

In watching my wild birds I found that with varying magnifications, I could pass through several stages of optical intimacy. To the naked eye, as I have said, the shore birds on the farther side of the beach were only a group of wading birds, but even with the lowest power glasses there began to emerge what I like to call the species behavior, or specific personality, quite apart from color and pattern, and even size. For example, one eighth day of September, when there were many kinds of waders on the beach, I made the following action and psychological key, which when given to members of my staff to use, proved as effective for identification as details of color and size revealed through much higher magnifications.

SPOTTED SANDPIPER: Comparatively deliberate, not at all wary, the rather stout body constantly teetering.

SEMIPALMATED SANDPIPER: Nervous but not wary, moving in short, running spurts, pecking but seldom, always retrieving a morsel of food; constantly fighting or pretending courtship.

LEAST SANDPIPER: Very tame, seldom on guard, movements more irregular than preceding, pecking constantly, only now and then finding and swallowing food; never fighting, often taking advantage of turnstones' activities in uncovering food.

SANDERLING: Constantly drilling deep holes, one after another, seldom merely pecking; usually near water line.

TURNSTONE: A waddling walk, feeding by pushing weed over; butting it with the head.

PIPING PLOVER: Timid, nervous, large eyes never off guard, snatching food quickly, near water; time spent watching to time of feeding, about 20 to 1.

SEMIPALMATED PLOVER: Still more timid, long intervals of watching; feeds higher up the beach, at every stop one leg lifted very slightly.

Some day we will know much more about these phases of animal life — where the spirit of the flock merges into specific personality; and when and why this, in turn, gives way to the unrestricted interplay of individual emotions and mental reactions.

The turnstones were the most abundant and regular beach birds. It seems settled that they do not breed in Bermuda, yet they are the earliest to arrive and the last to be seen. Three notes from my journal reveal an interesting happening — all the more inexplicable if all the birds are migrants.

September 7th, 1929 — Seventeen turnstones on South Beach, two of which are cripples. One, a

29. The bird blind at South Beach, Nonsuch, and the giant binoculars in action.

30. Nestling Yellow-billed Tropicbird or Longtail.

female, has the right foot bent far over and stiffened. The other is a male and has lost the entire right foot, toes and metatarsus, the limb having healed at the tarsal joint. The plucky bird balances perfectly and stumps easily about, feeding and holding its own in every way. Strangest of all, its fellows often quarrel among themselves over a rich find of sand-hoppers, but all give way to the cripple.

June 7th, 1930 — Nine turnstones on South Beach, one of them the identical cripple seen a year ago, a male in normal plumage.

May 17th, 1931 — Three cripples among a flock of ten birds. Two of these I saw in 1929 and one last year. A diagram I made at the time, of the peculiar arrangement of the inbent toes of the female and a hardened, inward projecting flap of skin seen at the stump of the male's leg, leave no possibility of doubt of the individual identity.

August 17th, 1931 — Of four turnstones, three are cripples, one a new one with the left leg hanging loose, swinging about, so the bird has either to hop or squat flat. It is a male in good plumage, and feeds as well as a normal bird. The tarsal-stump male is the same seen in 1929 and 1930.

We know how the slightest handicap of abnormal structure or even color is usually soon fatal to a bird, slain either by keen-eyed hawk or by the savage assaults of its own kind. Yet here were birds migrating year after year, holding their own and undisturbed by members of their flock; cripples with a distorted foot, a dislocated upper leg, or actual loss of one leg.

I have never seen these birds pragmatize their name, probably because I have never observed them on a rocky beach, but here they eternally merit the name Turnweeds. While far less dainty and trim and graceful in outline and gait than the other shore birds, yet their plumage is always immaculate and undisturbed, and as far as actual beauty of pattern and brilliance of pigment go, their harlequin rufous, black and white plumage is supreme among the birds of the beach. Yet alone, among all of their relatives, they spend most of their time butting and pushing and shoving against the half-dried sargassum weed, in spite of which, with the most powerful glasses, I can never see a disarranged feather on their foreheads or a dirty or bedraggled plume on breast or wing. This unique habit of searching for and finding food brings about very definite relations with many of the other birds.

The scene on October 3rd, 1931, well illustrated this. A fairly strong northeast wind was blowing from inland across the beach and this, plus a hard-working shock troop of turnstones, resulted in an amusing interrelationship of the birds in sight. Six turnstones were crowded in the lee of a great stranded log, all butting and straining, head down, at the windrow of weed. They of course reaped a rich harvest. The birds were less than two hundred feet away and with my 20-powers I could readily distinguish even the varying colors of the cloud of sand-hoppers which arose at each rolling over of a bunch of weed. The beaks of the turnstones worked like pistons, each down-thrust representing the diminution of the race of *Orchestia platensis* by one. These unfortunately over-edible little beings have themselves travelled far over the world, probably clinging to weed and driftwood, and today they range from Nova Scotia to Brazil and are also at home on the shores of the Mediterranean.

As the turnstones rolled their weed on this windy day, hundreds of the sand-hoppers leaped so high into the air that they were caught by the wind and carried down over the white sand. Four leasts, a semipalmated and a sanderling scurried and ran, first rushing up close to the log, then, as a barrage of hoppers passed overhead, they would fan out and tear down the beach, chasing and finally capturing the particular game they had selected. I could tell the direction and the number of leaps of the crustacean by the dodgings and stops of the feathered hunter. Now and then a particularly sporting *Orchestia* would leap and be wind-blown to the very ocean's edge, when one of the sandpipers would wade into the ripples breast-high to retrieve it.

Low down on the beach a solitary cool-gray piping plover and an equally exquisite and dainty semipalmated plover fed in their timid, hysterical way. They were too dignified to chase sand-hoppers. With my telescope I could see every feather, every fearful glance of their great eyes, and could even detect the three kinds of worms which they were unholing. The belted plover would have made friends and tried to feed close to his paler cousin, but the piper would have none of it and missed many a toothsome worm by constant pursuit of his fellow.

On a windless day when the birds spray out more along the beach, each turnstone has an attendant pair or trio of sandpiper camp-followers. The least are the most impudent and fearless. They fairly get between the legs of the turnstones and dash in at the first hint of moving weed, as the larger birds brace themselves to shift it. The other sandpipers hang about the outskirts of the gastronomic game of rugby, but none ever learns to butt or push the weed aside for himself. It is as exclusive a characteristic of the turnstones as is their bandy gait and parti-colored feathers.

On Nonsuch we have a radio which we never use, a telephone which functions only in case of vital need, papers from the outside world reach us a week late and no one minds. Our work is too absorbing seriously to miss contact with the rest of the planet, but when the last tropicbird leaves its home in the cliffs, and the ultimate crippled turnstone rises from the beach and sets its course out to sea, Nonsuch becomes a little desolate. We cherish our seabirds and we love our tourists in feathers.

CHAPTER IX

THE joys of exploration are as varied as the numbers and characters of the explorers themselves, and the joys change during the lifetime of each person. I can remember the time when my greatest ambition was to be the first to step upon some tropical desert island, or to penetrate to where no white man's foot had ever trod. Then came the period of peripatetic journeys, of covering as much ground as possible in a given time. But I soon found that the island might be " desert " in very truth, with no return in scientific loot, and the thrill soon passed of encircling a sandy spit and seeing none but one's own footprints. I came to learn that worthwhile observations of birds and animals and insects were great in proportion to the smallness of territory covered. One might shoot a large parrot or catch a brilliant butterfly as one travelled, but to go slowly or to sit quietly was to invite the acquaintanceship of many rare and interesting creatures. To be a good naturalist one must be a stroller or a creeper, or better still a squatter in every sense of the word — never a traveller.

Then came joys within joys. For to be a squatter alone is only the beginning. We can divide our observations into static and dynamic. We can wait for hours and days for the glimpse of a bird, or for the courtship of a spider, or spend a whole night of the full moon in hopes of seeing a jaguar or a yapock, not from the point of view of a man, but from that of another jaguar or another water opossum. This method is of vital importance, and probably four-fifths of creative study of life histories must be gleaned in this manner. But there remains a residue of technique which excels all: one-fifth we will call it, because our poor, city-crippled muscles and senses will seldom permit more. It is the supreme achievement, the essence of intelligent deduction, which, when successful, brings to us a great feeling, never of conceit or egotism, but of gratitude, of awe, at having been permitted somewhat to enter into the very life feelings and intimate habits of wilderness folk.

A vocal bond is an unforgettable relationship. It is probable that every creature which has ears and can become audible, has some sound to which it will react at once, and toward which it will immediately fly or run or creep or hop. With the miserable range of whistled or uttered tones which is our degenerate heritage we can rarely command or put this into practice. One of my first successes was the master sound of the chickadee. One could whistle chicka-dee-dee-dee-dee until Parus-perfect and be rewarded by hardly a turn of the head. But in an unseasonable February thaw, when one felt spring and dreamed spring, but knew better than to say Spring, if we wetted our lips very carefully and holed down to finest whistle diaphragm, the resulting high, two-toned *phœ-be!* might bring a black-cap to our very face. My happiest refinement of this was when I learned to bring a jungle wren of the genus *Leucolepia* to my feet from a quarter mile distance across a tropical swamp, by a single, almost inhumanly high tone: And this is one of the wariest of wrens, most difficult to stalk. I derive a keen, childish joy from the knowledge that if today I enter a tropical jungle and send forth a high, thin penny-whistle of a sound on exactly E flat above middle C, every sloth within hearing will either answer or slowly and painfully begin to turn in my direction. A half tone above or below will be the same as silence to these creatures, and I feel mentally the richer for knowing the utterly useless fact of the exact master sound of the sloths.

Another type of achievement, perhaps not as difficult, is to penetrate not only to the haunts in general, but to the exact abode of a species or individual by forehand knowledge or by deduction of a sight, sound, odor or the significance of some particular habit, only indirectly connected with the individuals sought. To such belonged the accomplishment of my desire for an adequate collection of jungle water-beetles, when months of search had revealed only two or three specimens. Amid the jeers of my staff I planted dishpans and tubs here and there in the heart of the tropical jungle, sank them to a level with the ground, filled them with water, and thereafter each morning made my rounds, like a Canadian fur trapper, reaping a harvest of rare and unknown tropical coleoptera of many species and countless individuals. And this with two large rivers flowing past within a few hundred yards.

This very year my friend Dr. Conklin wished to time his visit to Nonsuch by the breeding of Amphioxus or Lancelets, and soon after landing I sent out an assistant with pail, a rope, a rowboat and an outboard motor, in the certain knowledge that several hauls over an exact area of fathom deep sand to the northeast of Nonsuch would yield a supply of these supremely interesting beings.

This preamble may serve as introduction to the last application of this general idea in my studies of the bird life of Nonsuch. The yellow-billed tropicbird nests everywhere on the cliffs in almost every available hole and crevice, but as far as we knew no other seabird breeds here.

Night after night, throughout all the spring months we have been here, when dark closes down, there come through the murk from the direction of the open sea strange voices — sweet, modulated tones wholly unlike the metallic *pink!* or *tink!* of the tropicbirds. The calls are harmonious with no element of harshness, half tones following whole tones, while occasionally there rings out a trisyllabic, silvery minor chord: *whee-o! whee-whee-o!* I have wondered often at these disembodied Sirens, and finally I began to box them on the horizon of

140

31. Nestling Cahow or Audubon's Shearwater taken from its crevice nest on Idol Island.

32. Nest, egg, and nestling Cahow, from Green Island.

my blind, auditory compass. They came consistently from a narrow sector in the southeast and after a few nights of confirmatory repetition I shifted my observations one morning to a visible horizon and found that the source of the nocturnal voices included Green Island — the last continuation of Nonsuch beyond South Point.

During the first year of my stay I had wandered over this small, isolated, wave-worn patch which was about one hundred yards across, and had found nothing of especial interest. On the sixteenth of May of the year 1931 we visited it again. I leaped from the stern of a small boat as it balanced upon the summit of a rising swell, and swarmed up a cliff composed of effectively arranged, serried ranks of pins, daggers, needles, half-opened scissors, knives, nails, fish-hooks, arrows and bits of broken glass. It proved, after all, to be only a cliff of æolian sand, dissolved and refused and tempered to marble hardness, and sculptured and whetted to razor sharpness by the waves: but to hands and feet it was all the rest. The islet rose to a low, central table-rock by way of two diminutive and irregular terraces and its title was saved from absolute misnomer solely by a thin, emerald enamel of flattened and sprawling sea purslane with its tiny, purplish-pink faces staring up at the sky. Single and double pads of island cactus hid low among the scattered sea ox-eye and marine mulberry. No cedar today had been able to face the blasting salt and live, although stony molds here and there showed where great forests had stood on the island in unknown times past.

We had hardly begun to quarter the islet, when, on the very summit, thrown up by a breaker during some mighty storm, we found a pair of wings joined by the ivory-white shoulder girdle of some small seabird. Then our search was stimulated by the discovery of a bit of white eggshell far under a low ledge. A triumphant shout summoned me to the extreme southerly tip. Centuries upon centuries ago, when Nonsuch Bay was encircled by dry land, one of the greatest of cedars reared its foliage upon this spot. All that remained in this twentieth hundredth year of our calendar was the limestone outline of the trunk and large roots, all the details of the weathered contours being still distinct. It was easy to trace the meandering of the roots, to see where a mighty twist had been taken about some helping shoulder of rock — a rock long since dissolved — the straining of the plant muscles, which began ages before the times of the Egyptians, being still visible in the sunlight of today.

The great mineral bole stood up nearly three feet above the rest of the surface of the island and when I came closer, I saw it was hollow. I peered down, and after the excitement of bright sunlight had died down in my eyes I discerned in the heart of this marble tree the softest thing in the world — a downy chick. It was almost the hue of the twilight in which it lived, and was cozily squatting beneath a low, half-open ceiling of rock tracery. As I looked, something equally dark scuffled into view and my chick gave forth a series of high protesting cheeps as it wriggled from beneath the feet of its nervous mother. She turned a shining black eye up at me and waited for what this new adventure might bring forth. I could see her only in sections and what was visible led my ornithological mind first to sooty terns, then to Mother Carey's chickens.

We made certain that there was no half-hidden exit and that she must clamber up and down the hollow chimney of the prehistoric cedar. Then we found that it was impossible to reach her. Whenever I lowered my hand and arm she shuffled back a few inches and was as safe as if behind the strongest of steel bars. Only a mighty charge of dynamite would have dislodged her, while all I wanted was to make identification certain. The age of the young bird ensured another week or two of habitation so we left with reasonable hopes of seeing them again.

The sector of the aural compass extended somewhat to the east of Green Island, so on the following day we landed on Idol Island. This is separated from Nonsuch by a narrow strait, through which the tide flows back and forth in a restless stream fifteen feet in width. It is even smaller than Green Island — possibly one hundred feet across, and on the summit rises in solitary grandeur the stone idol which dominates the lacerating surface. Its expression and even its personality varies when viewed from different points along the Nonsuch shore and I have named five successive promontories after the

NONSUCH

gods whose profiles are suggested — Chubu, Bud-
dha, Kib, Anubis, Hanuman.

This islet I found the metropolis of these birds.
They proved to be Dusky or Audubon Shearwaters,
and are to Bermuda what the Flightless Cormorant
is to Albemarle, and the Heath Hen to Martha's
Vineyard — a bird on the point of extinction. Fossil remains of this and a very closely related petrel
have been found in crevices and caves of all the
surrounding islands. I have unearthed, or rather un-
sanded, a half dozen on Nonsuch.

On this tiny Idol Island I found five successes
and five failures among the shearwater nests. On
my first visit, a parent bird was sitting on an empty
nest, next time both birds were present and the third
time the crevice was vacant; two white eggs discovered the first time were later found to be deserted, although one was about to hatch and the
other was fresh. Two downy young with no parents
to guard them during the day, grew apace and at
last flew safely away, and a third young bird which
was constantly attended by one parent also sur-
vived. One shearwater had chosen a nesting place
in a deep crevice which could not possibly be
reached, but by sighting through lateral slits I
watched the young bird, and saw it last just before
it climbed up the narrow chimney and flew. Finally
an easily accessible shearwater was found on a half-
grown young. It was lifted up, examined, measured
carefully and replaced, and successfully reared the
youngster.

144

33. Longtail on nest and parent Cahow.

34. Longtail nesting near the fatal arch on Nonsuch.

CAHOWS AND LONGTAILS

The young birds were a pure culture of mouse gray fluff, with no visible feet, only a negligible glint of an eye and a wholly inadequate beak. They were paler below, but the dark gray of the upper parts was exactly the color of the weathered rocks. The parents were most simply and severely black above and pure white on the side of the head and all the under-parts. The eggs were the only conspicuous thing in the entire life of these birds — whitest of white.

Three weeks later when I swam through the rush of waters and crept up the sharp rocks of Idol Island, I found the youngsters rather disheveled, still downy superficially but with the real feathers well started beneath, and the wings sprouting rapidly. They were almost bald, the pin feathers of the scalp having started growth. They were fluffed out and looked obese and at least twice the size of the parents.

I have already mentioned the abundant remains of half-fossilized bones of these small petrels on all surrounding islands from Castle to St. David's, attesting their former abundance — bones of two species, of one of which only a single mounted specimen remains. Today I have heard Bermudian fishermen speak of these voices of the night as Cahows and the early settlers of these islands knew both species by this name.

Going back more than three centuries, one William Strachy on the fifteenth of July, 1610, wrote as follows concerning these little seabirds: " A kind of webbe-footed Fowle there is, of the bigness of an *English* green Plouer, or Sea-Meawe, which all the Summer wee saw not, and in the darkest nights of Nouember and December (for in the night they only feed) they would come forth, but not flye farre from home, and houering in the ayre, and oure the Sea, made a strange hollow and harsh howling. Their color is inclining to Russet, with white bellies, as are likewise the long Feathers of their wings Russet and White, these gather them-selues together and breed in those Ilands which are high, and so farre alone into the Sea, that the Wilde Hogges cannot swimme ouer them, and there in the ground they haue their Burrowes, like Conyes in a Warren, and so brought in the loose Mould, though not so deepe; which Birds with a light bough in a darge night (as in our Lowbelling) wee caught. I haue beene at the taking of three hundred in an houre, and wee might haue laden our Boates. Our men found a prettie way to take them, which was by standing on the Rockes or Sands by the Sea side, and hollowing, laughing, and making the strangest out-cry that possibly they could; with the noyse whereof the Birds would come flocking to that place, and settle vpon the very armes and head of him that so cryed, and still creepe neerer and neerer, answering the noyse themselues: by which our men would weigh them with their hand, and which weighed heauiest they tooke for the best, and let the others alone, and so our men would take twentie dozen in two houres of the chiefest of them: and they were a good and well relished Fowle, fat and full as a partridge. In January wee had great store of their Egges, which are great as an Hennes Egge, and so fashioned and white shelled, and haue no difference in yolke nor white from an Hennes Egge. There are thousands of these birds, and two or three Ilands full of their Burrowes, whether at any time (in two hours warning) wee could send our Cockboat, and bringe home as many as would serue the whole Company: which birds for their blindnesse (for they see weekly in the day) and for their cry and whooting, wee called *Sea Owle:* they will bite cruelly with their crooked Bills."

And now tonight in the late evening of June 7th, 1931, three hundred and twenty-one years later, I sit, probably within sight of the place where William wrote his excellent account, and there come to my ears the plaintive calls of the last of the Cahows. They may cling to their pitiful islet crevices for a few more years, for collecting ornithologists are rare in Bermuda, laws are strict, care-takers are vigilant, and the difficulty and danger of making a landing on these wave-beaten outer islands is considerable. The Cahow will forever remain to me as one of my successful pursuits of a sound in the night.

One day I chose to sit in the heart of a hollow cauldron of great boulders at the foot of a western cliff on Nonsuch. Purple, green — purple, green, the ocean stretches out beyond the jagged barrier in front, in successive streaks of violent color. The

147

horizon is clear except for the stegosaurus-like bulk of Gurnet's Head a half mile off. Not quite clear, however, for my eye catches a tiny dot, a less than period — my tug Gladisfen at the vanishing point of sea and sky, drawing her two miles of slender tentacle thread, strung with the sextet of tiny pocket nets through the cold blackness of the lower ocean.

To my left towers a massive arch carved out by wind and water and framing a vista of cliff and sea and distant cedars. Not far away are two other arches long since fallen in, and I look up at the weakest point of the colossal curve overhead and wonder whether I will be allowed to complete this sentence. Somewhere in its substance there is the deciding grain of sand, somewhere a certain wave is gathering strength; in some imminent or distant time-space a gentle wind is arising. At the appointed time, when all these three shall meet, the wave will splash up and loosen the grain of sand, the wind will blow it from its age-old support, and gravitation, patient gravitation, will have its way. Whether it happens before this page is completed, and uncounted tons of rock bury these eyes, hand and paper, or whether some successor ten thousand years from now will be enabled suddenly to cease worrying about the petty things of his life is of no importance. It is only certain that then as now, tropicbirds, quite indistinguishable from those of today will rush for the last time through the arch and hover excitedly over the fallen debris.

(On July fifteenth, three weeks after this was

written, an outer shelf above the arch fell and killed a tropicbird. A few days later I dug out the bird and found a downy nestling which had died of starvation in an inner hollow. This was the first tragedy of the arch; an infinitesimal inorganic climax bringing to a close one of the topmost twigs of the tree of organic evolution.)

Even more than hummingbirds, tropicbirds are beings of the air. Infinitely more than the birds of paradise do they deserve the name *apodus,* for neither legs nor feet are clearly to be seen and are used as little as possible.

In flight two small patches are visible flattened below against the base of the tail — the webbed toes tucked out of the way. They are hardly more in evidence when the owner alights on the water or when it enters its nest. Like the landing of an overweighted airplane, the entering of the nesting hole by a tropicbird is a serious affair. Three or four false attempts are usually made, before the trajectory and speed are adjusted to the wind, and the parti-colored chassis is deposited on a slight ledge or actually in the hole. The bird then wriggles and pushes forward, seal-like, until it disappears.

One of the most useless characters I can imagine is the long, attenuated central pair of tail feathers. It surely can be of no courtship value, for these birds court and mate in mid-air, almost always two males in fierce rivalry. Under these circumstances it is difficult to imagine any nice adjustment as to admired length, resiliency or sweep of the feathery ornaments. The plumes are exceedingly tough and rubbery, as they must be to resist the wear and tear of constant attrition against the narrow ledges and rocky tunnels.

The yellow-billed tropicbird is virtually the only seabird that nests in Bermuda, a fact wholly unreasonable to our human minds. For here are hosts of perfect nesting places on isolated islets and unclimbable cliffs; here is food — crabs, fish, squid — in abundance, and most important in these later days of evolution, here are iron-clad man-made laws to protect them. Yet gulls and terns, gannets and petrels hesitate or alight only to recover from stress of storms, and then go their way to Greenland or to Patagonia, according to the season's urge.

The tropicbirds call cousins such diverse beings as pelicans, snakebirds, cormorants and man-o'-war birds, and their voice is as unlike these as their bodies. The chronic syrinx abortion of the adult pelican leaves him only a sibilant hiss of air passing over untuned chords; the cormorants grunt and croak like giant frogs, the man-o'-war has a courtship cadenza, liquid as a song-bird's, but the trio of passing tropicbirds sends down to me only a harsh, metallic *tink! tink!* recalling the flock notes of cross-bills coming over a snowfield, or tree-frogs tinkling in the dusk of a tropical jungle.

Longtail is the Bermudian name for these black-and-white birds. They seem to change color as rapidly as the squid upon which they feed, for when they fly over our white-washed laboratory roof their breasts are as immaculate as snow; over the shallows their plumage takes on the faintest, most delicate of pale chrysoprase, and far out from land, where the water draws its color from a full mile depth of ocean, reflection touches the plumage with a bubble-thin tint of ultramarine. When we see a tropicbird in full plumage on its nest in sunlight, within arm's length, a new color impinges upon our retina — we can no longer call its breast and tail white, and we cannot say that they are salmon or pink — the delicacy of this new real tone survives no human-made name, it is sheer beauty.

In early March the tropicbirds appear and the fishermen know that all the squid will vanish, solely, as they think, because of the arrival of their domi-nant enemies. But somewhere there are still squid in abundance, for the crops of the birds bulge with them, caught far out at sea, and the young are fed chiefly on squid as well as flyingfish.

There must be some significance in the constant sight of three birds flying together. It seems pos-sible that there are more females than males, and that bigamy is not an uncommon event. On the other hand, fierce battles are waged over the females and I have sent my photographer to a ledge where two birds had been lying for a half hour, beak grasped by beak, wings bent and twisted beneath their bodies as they tumbled about or lay in angry ex-haustion. They paid no attention to the man when he photographed them and he finally picked them up and tore them apart. Even when both had been tossed out into the air they immediately resumed the battle on the wing.

They seem tireless in flight, and I have rarely seen them resting upon the water. Ten miles out at sea a solitary bird will now and then appear, and swoop low over the tug, dipping his ensign to his fellow neighbors of Nonsuch. Then he resumes his chiefest, but one, duty in life, his search for food, and when this is found he broad-arrows his whole being, and with gravitation for impetus, shoots down upon squid or fish. Such mastery over the air and sea have these tropicbirds that it is less wonderful that they can control their inner selves. The squid may be swallowed and digested at once. Or if it is intended as sustenance for mate or offspring it can be stored in the gullet. Hours later when it is decanted into the maw of the young bird it is as fresh as when newly caught.

As one walks along the cliff edge of Nonsuch or clambers up and down the diminutive canyons and Bad Lands near the water, a vocal mine is sprung now and then apparently beneath one's feet, a sudden unexpected, screeching, unoiled rattle which startles the calmest nerves. This is a parent tropicbird objecting with raucous protest to the invasion of her domain. The nearest crevice or tunnel shows her flashing eyes, and her yellow beak half open ready for able defense. We nudge her to one side and the immaculate contour of her breast is disturbed by a segment of purplish brown egg, or through the white feathers there pops a tiny head only less white because of the fluffiness of its down. Here we have an epitome of tropicbird development.

The parent explodes again and the downy infant echoes her in a weak and minor key. But there is a marked individuality and I have lifted some birds off their nest, examined and replaced them without eliciting a sound of remonstrance.

For two successive years on Nonsuch (1929 and 1930) there were fifty-seven occupied nests within climbing reach and probably thirty more on the northern cliffs beyond human approach. I banded parents with green and nestlings with red leg-bands and found that the young breed the second year, and in a few cases at least, the same birds return to the same nesting holes.

The slight variation in breeding season is shown by comparison of the two years:

	Eggs	Newly Hatched	$\frac{1}{4}$ Grown	$\frac{1}{2}$ Grown	$\frac{3}{4}$ Grown	$\frac{7}{8}$ Grown	Invisible	Empty
1929 July 17th	11	5	8	10	4	5	10	5
1930 July 29th	8		5	6	8	8	10	10

Those recorded as invisible were in long, winding tunnels where the birds could be heard but not seen.

Some of the nests were in exquisite positions, such as one little cave, with three entrances, divided from each other by two marble columns or completed stalactites, with overhanging flowering vines partly shielding the aperture. When the parent was absent one day, I climbed down from above, took a firm toe grip on a branch and let myself down until my head was well inside the hollow. The view through the vines and arched ways was very lovely, even upside down as I saw it and with a longtail chick thumping my nape. Lest we are tempted to endow tropicbirds with aesthetic tendencies let us remember the deep, dark, ill-smelling tunnels which form most of their homes, and realize that safety and accessibility are the real requisites.

Sometimes at midnight I have slipped out under the stars, made my way very carefully along the south shore path, and lying flat on the jagged ridge, listened intently. Before long there would come to my ears a subdued cheeping or a deeper note and I know that deep within the stone below me were tropicbirds and their chick, contentedly murmuring whatever tropicbirds murmur at midnight. And I thought of Nonsuch, not as my laboratory, nor even as one of the most beautiful of the Somers Isles, but as a great rugged pile of marble, with the hearts of twice one hundred birds beating deep within — birds which, three months hence, would be scattered far and wide over tropical waters. I went back into my own little cave of a room, and I knew that the longtails and I shared one very real emotion — love for our island.

CHAPTER X

M Y old-fashioned, half-centuried, beloved dictionary defines weather as " The state of the atmosphere with respect to heat, cold, dryness, moisture, wind, rain, snow, fog, etc." When I compare Nonsuch with New York City I realize that it is the weather which makes the most important difference and I believe it is the most difficult to write anything about. Instead of streets and houses and automobiles and people, I look out on sky and clouds and sunshine and sea and rocks and trees — and having thus listed the differences I find I have omitted weather. The most important atmosphere has been left out, perhaps because of its invisibility.

Weather is almost as personal a thing as rainbows, and we are bound by human sensations to reel forth words and sentences of how " I " feel under this or that condition. There is no help for it, we must make comparisons:

" And the wildest dreams of Kew are the facts of Khatmandhu,
    And the crimes of Clapham chaste in Martaban."

which is nothing compared with what you think of hot weather and what I think of hot weather, or how we individually react to a day of storm-driven

155

rain. In some of us, as in Aldous Huxley and myself, there lingers an inherited vestige of some ancestral rain-maker or medicine-man. Huxley's ancestor was a quack, a charlatan of sorts, since his
descendant writes, " Bugs — no; I am innocent of
bugs. But when it comes to bad weather I have to
plead guilty. Rain, frost, wind, snow, hail, fog —
I bring them to places where they have never been
heard of, at seasons when it is impossible they should
occur."

My ancestor Shaman, on the other hand, was top-
hole, infallible, for storms clear as I look up; when
I wish to go out, dense clouds vanish, when I desire
to work indoors the weather gets in all its so-
called disagreeableness. In twenty places " Beebe
Weather " is a by-word; once I was almost sub-
sidized to remain in London, so perfectly did I have
the weather under control! But I never think of
this in advance; I am conscious of my meteorologi-
cal mastery only afterwards, and am humbly thank-
ful that in thirty years I have never had a microscope or a valuable book even dampened in the
rainy season in the tropics.

I think one insuperable difficulty in thinking
clearly about the weather is its eternal change. It is
like watching the hands of a clock and trying to
write something exciting about them. For a year
and a half when I was a boy, I used to climb out
of a dormer window every late afternoon on to a
zinc gutter and in a most uncomfortable position
write a description of the sunset. The only thing I

recall now is that my sentences grew shorter and shorter toward the end of the eighteen months, which was encouraging, and that I learned to write without looking at the paper, because the color changed so quickly that if I took my eye away I was sure to miss something. It is this tangled mixture of weather and conscious passing of time that causes the trouble. My cedar tree is hastening toward its end through the same duration of time as a storm but compared with my life it might be an everlasting crystal. Reporting a dead calm or sheet lightning or a sunset is like covering a three-ring circus.

Another subtle thing about weather is its infinitely delicate gradations — the almost imperceptible merging of one phase into another. A squall can of course rise most abruptly, and the passing of the shadows of clouds is exceedingly rapid, but the transition of day to night in temperate latitudes often defies any spoken or written account — there is nothing definite with which to begin or end a phrase. Our most vivid impressions are those which come to us at the first impact of weather upon our newly awakened senses, or when we go out after many hours of concentrated indoor work.

Two days ago on the third of September when I woke as usual at half past five o'clock and went out to face my Nonsuch ocean, I found it a very early morning — early geologically. The earth seemed immature; winds and the strife of evolution had not yet been invented. To be sure there were tall

157

NONSUCH

green growths on Nonsuch and other islands but,
at the moment, having nothing with which to compare them, these cedars could well have been gigantic mosses and fungi. It was the inorganic world
which gave the dominant feeling of just beginning.
The sea was quiet, not even old enough to be stagnant — but as still as ever water can be. Even the
sunrise, having attained an exquisitely subdued
brilliance, hung fire in cosmic suspense and I also
held my breath. There was not a feather of wind —
the air was immovable and therefore unthinkable:
weather was on dead center.

It was not hot. The feeling of coolness — first hint
of the coming winter (only winters were still to be
thought of) added to the newness — the earth and
the sea had not had a chance thoroughly to warm up
after yesterday's tremendous experiment of making
the first water. And now I knew the dominant un-
derlying feeling — the earth was not revolving.
For a season it had ceased, was resting, — witness
the suspended sunrise — and the ether had stopped
rushing against the atmosphere. I knew it was only
for a morning or an hour — indeed the world might
begin its business of life and old age and death in
the next split second. But this experience would
never die in my memory. As long as I lived I would
remember the dawn when the earth stood still.
Somewhere, uncountable years from now, when
men began to clutter the earth, they were going to
believe that a certain general commanded the sun
to stand still. But that was simply to drag out a

battle. No man could ever believe in Joshua's cosmic feat as deeply as I believed in my early morning of the world.

On a day such as this, one has a sense of absolute intimacy with the universe; not the catch-phrase "oneness" with which certain forms of belief are sustained — nebulous, inarticulate mottoes, but something much nearer reality and definiteness. The earth and the sea and the sky and myself were shut safely together within four walls compounded of time and space. There were winds in the outside future, raging hurricanes, bitter chill, suffocating heat and the strife of fish and beast for food and mates — these would be going on sometime, but wholly outside a present something real and tangible. For once it was a world of absolute peace and rest, and my mind felt comfortable and at home. For once the need of clothing, the protection of human walls and roof were absent, and I stood alone on the middle of the top of my young Mother Earth and we both liked it exceedingly.

Yesterday I saw the official account of my day: Temperature, maximum 87.8, minimum 74.0; Sunshine, 10 hours, 10 minutes; Rain, trace; and I was pleased that my day would go down in the archives of meteorology as eminently satisfactory!

Since the first apeman learned to say to himself "I am I" he began to be articulate about the weather: the rising of the warm, life-giving sun and the devastating paths of hurricanes and lightning must have been the principal topics of interest in

NONSUCH

the Year of our Primates One, as they still are in
a considerable percentage of our conversation of
A.D. 1932. Our far distant ancestor mouthed a
couple of what he imagined were pleasing grunts;
we say " Good morning."

Man's attitude toward the weather has been
either that of a worshipper — to patronize the good
weather and appease the bad — or else an interested
bystander, helplessly realizing that the slightest
deviation from the normal would roast or freeze or
drown or starve the very last of his race from the
surface of the planet. It is of course the effects of
weather that concern him. To the atmosphere, still
and of equable temperature, man gives never a
thought although it is his very breath of life, but
he blesses the rain in spring and curses it in autumn;
frost is the boon of his grape, the bane of his orange
crop; winds bring health to him on land and destruction at sea; thunder and lightning may send
one human being rubber-booted, to hide in a feather
bed, while another, bare-headed, climbs to a hilltop,
drunk with ozone and the joy of elemental battle.

The Romans very practically crystallized their
ideas of weather and incidentally, via the Greek
αἰθήρ, gave us the word itself — by reasonably assuming that Æther was the son of Chaos and
Night — perhaps one of the several aliases of Ju-
piter who was the weather-man of Olympia.

The greatest fun to be gotten out of the weather
is to isolate a tiny slice of it and make it our own.
A cool puff of air on Nonsuch sometimes wakes me

160

35. Nonsuch in the calm of a perfect day.

36. Nonsuch quivering in the grip of a hurricane.

at dawn and I walk out and see a gentle tropical rain coming like a veritable mist across the bay — the lines appearing long before there is any sound or movement. I am still in shadow but the velvety drops have caught the first rays of the sun high in air and splintered them into a rather inadequate rainbow. This happens quite often in late summer and I have found a way of holding and enjoying its beauty long after the shower has passed and has left only the pungent, exciting smell of freshly-dampened, long-dried soil and foliage. I lower my sloping jalousie a few inches and there appear between the slats several hundred large diamond drops, wedged between the narrow bits of wood and afire from the sun rising just behind them. They last for an astonishing time, and only one by one are evaporated by the heat. I have come to watch with interest for the last living bead upon my elemental abacus. I have a favorite one which almost wins, but is usually beaten by another not perfect globe, which has the advantage of a slight nick in the slat which gives it an increase of content. One day I saw my pet drop striving to last, straining with all its surface tension to keep from losing its individuality and again to become an infinitesimal trinity of atoms. I could not stand being an idle pacifist any longer and reaching forward I deposited a finger-tip of shaving soap upon my particular jewel, which thereupon assumed a greater girth and a glory of iridescence, and was still a skim of beautiful water long after the site of its vanished rival had become dusty.

NONSUCH

This is one of a hundred silly games of personal weather. Besides the sheer joy of inventing and playing them at shaving time and other useless moments, they have many valuable by-products, like sending you to Jeans and Bragg and Eddington to find out why drops are and exactly where they go. The games are also a boon to anxious friends, providing food for speculation as to when I will probably become violent and whether I should not be confined at once.

Now and then a section of weather so detaches itself from that preceding and following, that it stands forever apart. Such was our first hurricane on Nonsuch. Its prelude was unusual but long-drawn-out, and it gave no hint of what was coming.

For ten days the weather had been perfect to the eye, comfortable to the skin, and ideal for my precious trawling operations; the sea calm, with frequent slicks, the gentle breeze, drifting in from the south, warm and delightful. No sargassum had come in, the weed fields of ocean were motionless, there was no sound among the cedars — their bent trunks had a long, long rest. After the tenth day of unusual dead calm, the sea rose, quite without visible reason. There was a breeze — zephyr would be the better name — which might raise ripples on a pond, yet the sea was troubled as in a stiff wind. For once I witnessed the effects of weather without the cause. With the disturbance came more brilliant colors than I have ever seen in these colorful waters. Sometimes, near Castle Island, a dozen diverse blues almost touch — today the shallows and the sea showed only two — but from the very ultimate, opposite limits of blue visible to human eyes. Near shore and out to the forty fathom line a half mile beyond Gurnet's Rock there was uniform, unbelievable, milky-pale turquoise, diluted almost to negative blueness; from these outermost shallows, along a line too even and sharp to be drawn by human instruments — from these to the horizon was rich, dark, ultramarine. Most amazingly all day, regardless of the altitude of the sun, these colors held unchanged, unoxidized.

The outer reefs were a narrow, continuous seam of purest white, bisecting the turquoise, and Gurnet was set in a smother of foam. As far as Nonsuch was concerned there might as well have been no outer reefs, for the windless rollers came in unchecked, rising, curving, holding aloft for a full second of eternity, and at last breaking on the marble cliffs — with a ringing crash on exposed rocks, a deep-mouthed thundering against the hollow caves and archways.

South Beach was not recognizable as the beach of yesterday; the ten days of quiet wash had swept the whole expanse clear of sargassum, so that the turnstones and sandpipers had to glean from a scanty supply of beach-fleas high up among the prostrate morning glories and sea lavender. Here, at the upper edge of high tide, a straggly line of sun-greyed weed still lay, like the tonsure of some aged monk.

Today, the sand was again covered, not with sargassum but with strange leathery, long-leaved kelp and rainbow-banded algæ torn up by unseen watery forces. Great rollers gathered force, like charging lines of cavalry, filling the little bay from cliff to cliff. Here at last they could use their strength to the utmost, and work the havoc which seems the sole purpose of heaving water. Higher and higher they rose, changing from opaque to translucent emerald and finally that unnamed hue born of equal mixture of sea and sky and air, and then — they sank quietly, unbroken, slithered a little distance up and back into the curve of the next potential wave. Not until I walked out into the water did I discover the reason for this sudden fiasco, these unbreakable breakers; — there was a solid zone of the kelp, self-colored with the water, which made of the thin, active liquid a thick, molasses-like soup. These were some of the changes which came about with no apparent wind to cause them.

At ten o'clock on the evening of August twenty-fourth, I was interrupted for a moment while looking at something which was five quintillions (or, to put it so that you can immediately grasp it; five billion billions) of miles away. My lips were mumbling these figures, and my brain was vainly striving to formulate some intelligent response. But there was at least a deep feeling of awe and humility. One could get flashes of the kindly, indulgent humor with which mankind's frantic strutting and his bab-

Photograph by E. R. Sanborn.

37. Shark-sucker clinging to the breast of a shark.

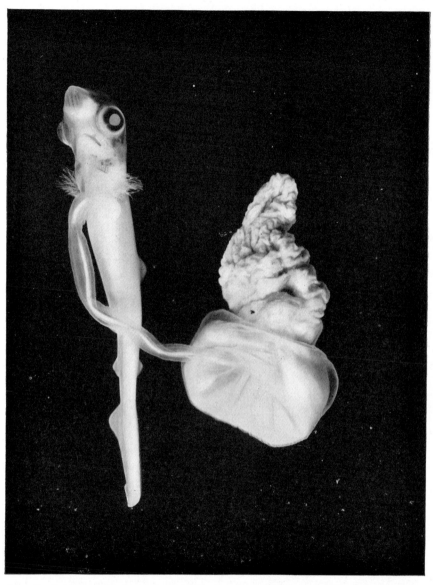

38. Great Blue Shark embryo. Observe the perfect mouth and fins, the
large eyes, external gills and yolk sac.

blings about individual equality and exact geographical boundaries must engender in a Creator, or a God, or even a Peasant with sufficient longevity. As a panacea for a host of human ills and worries and fears, I think I should advocate a law that every tooth-brush should have a small telescope in its handle and the two used equally. Five minutes' compulsory evening concentration through opera-glass or telescope by every King, President, M.P., Senator, Mayor, Lawyer, Soldier, Merchant, Farmer, Student and Ordinary Human, would bring the millennium as near as any of us want it, and an observatory on the roof of every prison and church would, I believe, aid respectively, in a very marked emigration and immigration.

However, to bring down the other foot upon the earth again, the slight cloudiness upon my telescope lens could easily have been made by a light breath, but was actually the greatest of all nebulæ, the spiral one in Andromeda; nine hundred thousand light years away (as I have already said). And when it was suddenly effaced I snatched my consciousness away from the magic lens and saw a black cloud — black even against the moonless heavens, and the cloud was coming too fast and from the wrong direction and it worried me.

For ten days since the long calm, a steady, hard wind had blown from the southwest, too strong for me to let my tug go to sea. Then it shifted to the northeast, coming with equal force. Then it died down — and now later in the evening it had swung to an unusual point of the compass — southeast. Yet the sunrise was fair and as usual as such an ever-new event can be. But all day the wind blew from the new quarter and with ever-increasing velocity. By mid-afternoon there arose, beyond the sea, a quarter heaven of sulphur gray clouds which looked too sinister to ignore. As I watched them a hunch came, and this materialized into a suggestion, then into an order, and we towed three of the five boats around to the beach. Here we man-powered them on skids along the sand and up the steep bank among the cedars.

The wind had increased so that the whole level of the ocean seemed higher, and at mid-tide the crashing breakers reached far above high-tide mark. They swirled up our bathing beach, sending angry fists of foam far up among the cedars after the boats as if angry at having lost their small, rightful prey. At Idol Island the waters met from two directions and shot up geyser-like high into the air. For the first time since I walked along the great cliffs of the Singhaleela Range within sight of Everest I leaned full weight upon the wind. Such a steady, strong current of air swept up Kib Promontory that I let my body slant far out against it — not a very sensible thing if a moment's calm should intervene. But none of us was quite sane on this day. The howl of the wind, the roar of the waves, the electricity and ozone in the air excited us beyond normal; no one thought of cocktails at dinner time — Weather took their place.

MILORD THE WEATHER

In late afternoon the sulphur and smoky-black shut down a little and the world became more and more somber. Then, to show us what it could do, Weather ripped the curtains apart and we were blinded with a glorious sunset of rose peach and sheer gold, setting on fire all the drops and salt crystals in the world, and for a time my ears refused to continue to register the uproar, so deadening to all other senses was the superlative brilliance and splendor of color in the west. It was quenched as abruptly as it appeared, and now when the low-hanging menace of whirling clouds showed a rent or a tear, the clear sky beyond was a sickening green.

Weather pondered for a moment, and then turned on the rain and for two hours it poured, yet the waves and wind never ceased. We battened down all windows and blinds and had settled to a long evening of work when word came up that the Sea-Fern, our breakwater, and the wharf were flooded.

We rushed down and by the flickering light of electric torches saw a hundred possessions bobbing about or drifting off on the raging tide — boxes, diving-helmets, barrels of gasoline, buoys, fish traps. Our strongest swimmer took a rope out to the most valuable and we hauled them back. The tide had still three hours to rise.

Posting a watch on the launch, I returned, and went the rounds every hour until three-thirty, when a sinister scarlet eye appeared on the signal station three miles away — warning that a hurricane was

167

on its way. Primitive man was our equal and contemporary as to fear and respect for Weather in this mood, and I routed out the staff and packed up all valuable records, instruments, books and specimens; during the last hurricane half the roofs had gone and we could afford to take no chances.

At the first hint of dawn we stripped the Skink, and sent the brave little launch across the three miles of reef and smothering foam, to the one safe bay near St. Georges where every boat at this end of the island scuttles to safety. We shouted good luck and watched our last means of communication with the outside world vanish in the dusk of the pale green dawn. We were alone on Nonsuch with the beginning of a hurricane.

There was no morning or afternoon — the light flickered, flaring and dimming — all sense of time went, only the wind steadily increased. I crept from building to building, attended by a hammer-and-nail-and-board companion, fastening a loose window here, putting another cross-bar there.

Once I went up on the sheltered cliff, but could see nothing clearly. I alarmed a cardinal which flew up from a sage-bush at my side, and at about ten feet elevation might as well have been struck with a full charge of shot, so completely was it whelmed by the rush of wind, dashed over and over and out into the deadly maelstrom of water in the bay.

It was impossible to face the wind, the drops of water and sand stung like hot shot, the pain was unbearable. I had two of my staff hold a piece of glass so that I could look through it. Once in a while I caught sight of Gurnet's Rock through the waves; Castle and the other islands did not visually exist. I could see no water anywhere — only foam, spindrift, and spray which rose and was carried over our heads at least a hundred feet above the level of the sea.

For another day and a night we dared not slacken our efforts, and then the wind and sea gradually went down and a morning broke clear and calm. Weather had only played with us after all, trying us out with the fringe of one side of the real hurricane. The wind was reported as not reaching hurricane force — having attained *only* 72 miles an hour! I recalled a typhoon in a Chinese junk and offered up thanks to Weather that we had been let off so easily.

Birds crept out from hiding places, daring to preen themselves and search once more for food, a torn butterfly sunned itself, preparing for its few remaining days of life; the goldenrod was beaten flat, the sage-bush lifted bare, dead stems. A thick carpet of berries and needles covered the island, but not a cedar had fallen: since birth they had prepared for just such crises as this. So I thought until I made a careful round of the island and then I found two which had been uprooted but had dropped upon the shoulders of sturdy comrades. It seemed as if the years of mutual strife for sun and soil had developed a close kinship among these gnarled trees, and here, like wounded elephants supported by a comrade, the stricken pair had not been allowed to reach the ground. The strength of their rescuers promised long life to both; the ranks of the cedars had closed up, the hurricane could claim no victory.

To those who have led sheltered lives it seems natural to speak of " the weather "; to us more fortunate ones, who have endured heat, suffered cold, fought through hail and snow on high Himalayas, wagered and won heavy odds with a dozen yards of undertow; who in night and fog have prayed from an airplane for at least soft branches, have risked everything on a few mouthfuls of rain falling not too late; and in addition, what is equally important, have marvelled at each sunrise and sunset and secretly uncovered at every miracle rainbow — to us it is not natural to speak of " the weather." We have learned to say Weather with a capital and in a whisper, and are not ashamed to imitate our early apemen forebears and to personify the glories and terrors of the atmosphere, the æther — the work and the play of Milord the Weather.

CHAPTER XI

THE DESTINY OF A BLUE SHARK

ON September twelfth I met a Great Blue Shark in the prime of life. A famous ichthyologist writing of the length of life of fish, says that " most of them grow as long as they live, and apparently live until they fall victims to some stronger species." By this criterion the blue shark whose path crossed mine on this September day could easily lay claim to a century, with excellent hopes of at least a millennium. But theories are always better when halved, so we will be safer if we suppose that my shark was born in July, 1877. That allots him a reasonable span of years, satisfies the verities of generalizations, affords no chance for contradictory proof of the mensal details and makes the splendid creature my contemporary. There is a record of a blue shark within ten miles of my birthplace so we have considerable in common.

His recognition by binominal taxonomic ichthyologists occurred a century earlier, one hundred and nineteen years to be exact, when Linnaeus officially named his great-grandfather, *Glauca,* as these sharks had been appropriately called by fishermen for hundreds of years before. In the course of time, after a change or two, *Prionace* was offered as his

171

generic name, meaning saw-pointed, with reference to his teeth.

Throughout historical times the blue shark has been described as a strong, swift swimmer, an inveterate man-eater, with a hide which makes the very best leather. This sums up most of our knowledge of his life-history, although long before Linnaeus happened to notice him, the above-mentioned fishermen had paid him much closer attention, occasionally calling him names which could not occur in any scientific catalogue.

While the two miles of wire and nets were being pulled in on the aft deck of the Gladisfen, our particular blue shark appeared from the equally blue depths. His color marked him as a true inhabitant of the open sea, like the flyingfish and the tunnies. But unlike them, there is no reason why blue sharks should not descend to great depths, and the Gladisfen individual may have come from a hundred or from five hundred fathoms for all we know. He appeared interested in the wire but swam steadily ahead — all four of them in fact, since he was not alone, but was accompanied by three friends, a remora or shark-sucker, who is one of the world's most amazing fish, and a brace of pilotfish.

The curiosity of our convoy was mild and he was content to swim slowly along, first to port, then to starboard. A shark is probably the most graceful animal in the world, and if you are the kind of person to think of such phrases as the poetry of motion, watching the blue shark in action is as good a time as

39. Land Crab in position of attack, and (lower) blowing out a mass
of acrid bubbles as a last means of defense.

40. A group of Wanderer Crabs, *Planes minutus*, showing extremes of variation in pattern.

any to think of it. The movement is wholly without effort: it is impossible to say where upon its body there is stress and where there is rest. The whole advance is along the line of rhythm of a wave length, which, for grace and efficiency, seems peculiar to these beings. If there is need for an instantaneous shooting ahead or a right-angled turn to left or right, the long, arched tail waves somewhat more quickly or in a wider swath, and we see that the blue shark is master of the three planes of space after a fashion which makes darius-greens of birds.

Throughout most of his existence the progress of this shark had been a wonderful, slow, undulatory weaving, through miles and miles of blue water, his species circling the globe in the warmer parts of the oceans. No blue shark may have been visible for days and yet at the death of a whale, they converge like vultures, hundreds of them, the first by sight and smell, the others by suspicion of the actions of some fellow shark who is doing what they would do if they had scented or sighted a prospective banquet.

Essentially, however, they are solitary wanderers on the face of the waters. They seldom approach land, and when the shallows bring the bottom nearer, or the roar of the breakers comes to their chalky earbones, they sheer off to sea again. But occasionally they find manna ready for the picking, where some unlucky fisherman has stretched his great length of mackerel net. Up and down the meshes goes the blue shark, snatching a bite every yard. Now and then a piece of net gets into his jaws, but his teeth are serrated and double-edged, and two or three skillful shearings clip the net clean away and it is swallowed with the fish.

For the first fifteen minutes of our life together the great blue shark attended the stern of the tug. The two pilotfish, unusually large ones, over a foot long, kept always one on each side of his dorsal fin, swerving not an inch, but shifting with each lateral swing of their master as if all three were strung on the same invisible wire. They too were blue, deep blue alternating with paler bands.

While the shark swept evenly ahead, its little sucking-fish slithered up and around, backward and forward, over all its body. Sometimes the three-inch sliver of black life would appear near the tip of the high dorsal fin, then down and across the gills, under the great belly and up on the opposite side. What an astonishing life — to have one's whole being fashioned to adhere to some great shark, by means of a sucking disk on top of the head. It reminded me of old geography pictures of a diminutive earth, always showing the heathen Chinamen walking upside down on the under side, while we, more enlightened Nordics of sorts, stalked about with our heads right side up in the air! As the three planes of watery space are magicked into one by the shark, so gravitation seemed non-existent to the remora — up, sideways, or down were all the same to him. His planet was a living one, a great elongate spindle with eight slender promontories of fins; his air and sky — the ocean; his food — the crumbs which dropped from the meals of the shark.

The Gladisfen's cook threw over some boiled potatoes, no other bait being available. The great shark turned toward and nosed them, then dropped back. One of the pilotfish deserted for a moment, returned and snapped at the drifting vegetable, and again a second time, its fellow not moving from its place. Then the shark approached close under the stern counter, and deigned to swallow some of the inappropriate food; a medium-sized hook on a cod line was dropped over, taken and when jerked, caught on the lip of the huge fish. A single sideways nod, and hook and line would have torn out or broken, yet the shark allowed his head to be lifted high enough for a full-sized shark hook to be dropped in, swallowed and firmly hooked. Now, too late, the great animal began to fight, but a skillfully thrown wire noose held the great tail helpless. The pilots kept off a yard or two, but the suckingfish still slithered over his world which threatened to be engulfed in the unimaginable medium of air. A scoop of the net captured him, and he exchanged the comfortable roughness of shagreen for the less holdable inner surface of a pail.

The shark was hauled on board, and before long the deep-sea nets were pulled in, and the tug headed full speed for Nonsuch. Throughout three or four miles of fast steaming the pilotfish kept pace; their lord had, for reasons best known to himself, chosen to desert the water and ascend to the sky. This noisy monster, greater than even their shark, had received him, and for mile after mile they followed faithfully. Then the bond, which had been so close and for whose reason and mutual advantage the most learned scientist can only hazard a guess, became less strong, more tenuous, and finally the last strand broke, and the two pilotfish, after one or two uncertain half returns, dived from our sight forever. Pilots without a ship, did they keep together or separately search for another berth?

In the water the great blue shark stirs us to enthusiasm over the grace of his movements, but not until I studied him outstretched full length on our wharf did I realize how marvelous was his form. Even without the equalizing balance of buoyancy of the water, pressed down by the overwhelming pull of gravity in the air, even so, his outline was very beautiful; long, slender, stream-lined to a supreme degree of delicacy and efficiency, which would be meaningless in a yacht; his fin keels for steadying and orienting, the mighty upward-reaching tail and the enormously elongated, graceful pectorals. These wonderful falcate fins are models for all swift-swimming fish of higher grade, and have been imitated by those aquatic backsliders, seals, whales and penguins. And now I realized that I should have followed the ancient custom of the sea, and when I began to dilate on the beauty of curve and grace of movement of the fish, I should have spoken as one does of a beautiful ship, of *her*

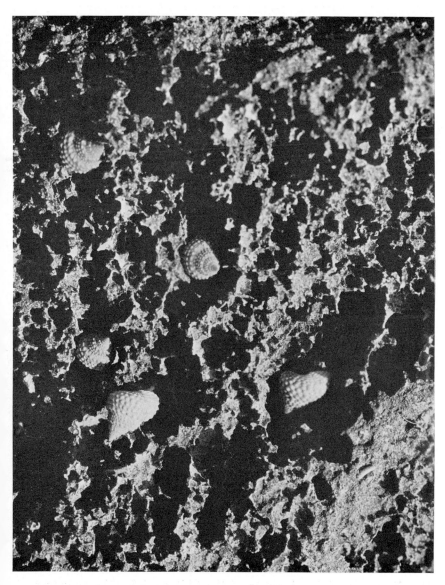

41. The way of a Snail upon the rocks.

42. Where the jointed armor of the Chitons defies the pounding of the surf.

— for now I saw that my great blue shark was a female.

The sucking-fish was safe in its pail, but I soon found we had captured more than two creatures. On the under side of one of the long pectoral fins, near its base, I saw tiny beings scampering over the rough skin, and I began to gather in a whole colony of parasitic crustaceans, strange little creatures whose life history outdoes Grimm, Dunsany and Alice. Here were two and fifty of these copepods, all clustered in a single village on the waving fin. This exposure to incessant movement insured of course an excellent supply of running water, but I should think such admirable plumbing arrangements would be more than counterbalanced by the constant danger of being scraped off into the middle of the ocean. They were pale yellow below, dark seal brown above, this upper surface bearing a surprising likeness to a black mask with eye-holes of buff. Their dorsal plates were much like the skin denticles of the shark, although why they needed such protection I cannot imagine. If shark-suckers were fond of copepods nothing could save them, but no other living creature would dare approach a blue shark for any such purpose. The legs and other appendages of the small crustaceans were a maze of vacuum cups, explaining their gliding ability. The females had two trailing ropes of eggs, and I tried to imagine the adventures of an infant copepod loosed on the high seas, and the probability of his meeting and fastening upon a suitable shark home.

NONSUCH

All that came to me was a new simile — as slender as a baby copepod's chance of life.

Two things I have always regretted, first, that the ethics of social manners have always forbidden my exclaiming over the delectable odor of my hostess' dinner — course by course; and secondly that it is seemingly impossible to write of the beauty of such a sight as was afforded by the interior of the body of the blue shark. Years and years in the open have doubtless sharpened my sense of smell beyond what one usually possesses with propriety, and as to internal organs, the tints and shades, the forms and arrangement are so wonderful, together with the adaptations and perfect correspondence to outward shape, habits, food and method of feeding, that a detailed account would be anything but an anatomy of melancholy. Only ancestral and ontogenetic habits prevent me from having a try. It is an amusing world where anyone would peruse with interest the details of a shark's heart, the mind recalling poetry and valentines, whereas the exquisite color of the gall-bladder and the fine architecture of the spiral valve far transcend the first mentioned organ, which is exactly as far distant from the seat of the emotions as it is from the brain.

It is difficult to omit mention of the stomach for it was no longer an internal organ, but was inverted and protruding from the mouth, looking like a many-folded tongue. I saw a bit of bright color and found it was a large and beautifully shaped jaw of a squid. I pried open the mouth a little and ex-

178

tracted a large white squid with the other half of its jaw, together with two boiled potatoes. This extrusion of the stomach is not at all connected with death, but is a very convenient arrangement to enable the shark to get rid of such indigestible relics of a meal as fish bones and squid jaws. It recalls the neat little oval pellets of bones and fur which we pick up beneath owls' nests.

I gave one last tug at the jaws and one of the smaller teeth cut through my finger as if it were a newly-sharpened razor.

The teeth are very beautiful, a front row of thirty in each jaw, recurved triangles in the upper and upright spearheads in the lower. They are of the finest polished ivory and toothed all the way around — half a hundred razor-edged scallops. Behind the upright row is a deep depression or trench to which might be given the name of the dentist's despair, for it holds an infinity of reserve teeth, ready to spring to place when required. Everything about the teeth is ingenious. They overlap, but not like the tiles on a roof, when if one was broken they would all weaken, but every other one is wholly outside, and the two adjoining inside. When one of the outer ones breaks off or is lost, its nearest reserve in the second line trench is drawn upright by strong membranes and the line is unbroken. At the deepest end of the trench, the teeth are soft and leathery and still farther back they are mere creases or folds in the wall.

My anatomist and I were not nearly so familiar

with the details of a shark's internal anatomy as with those of other fishes, but we made a preliminary rough dissection and measured and weighed several organs, including one apparently empty, elongate ovary. Delving deeper into the white body chamber I brought up a strange organ with an unaccountable shape, an organ to which we could not give a name. I placed it in a deep pan and at my first incision, there emerged a perfectly good diminutive shark. When after him there trailed a yolk sac like a collapsed parachute I realized that my ideas of sharks' ovaries needed revision. Further search revealed the second ovary equally large.

Later, at leisure, I investigated and found twenty-five embryos in each ovary. So here was at last the tale of the catch — not a single shark, but the pair of pilots which got away, a sucking-fish, fifty-two strange little crustaceans and fifty-one sharks — a goodly collection of one hundred and six individual animals: My great blue shark was less a fish than a mother, an aquarium and a zoological garden combined.

While men throughout the ages have probably more frequently cursed than admired the blue shark, there are delightful bits on record of attributes more charming than veracious.

Eighteen centuries ago Oppian in his classic *Halieutica* wrote of our shark as follows:

" Of all oviparous kinds that throng the sea,
The fond Blue Sharks in tender care surpass.

180

THE DESTINY OF A BLUE SHARK

They rear their fondlings, like some careful nurse,
Observe their motions and restrain their course,
Eye every wave, and shew the doubtful way,
Teach where to hunt, and where to find their prey.
When big with secret guilt the waters heave,
They in their mouths their shelter'd young receive,
But when the waves at their own leisure roll,
And no fierce robber drives the scatter'd shoal,
Again the parent's pointed jaws compress'd,
By force expel them from their pleasing rest."

It is a delightful idea and there is no objection to
belief in it, if one does not demand proof or probability. There is no doubt of the attachment between
parent and young sharks. In diving I have watched
a mother shark and two young swimming together,
week after week. The pair of youngsters sticking as
close to her as pilotfishes. And I have seen a mother
and father cichlid fish in Guiana take their entire
brood of one hundred or more into their mouths for
protection, and puff them out again unharmed
when danger is past, but, *quod erat non demon-
strandum,* these facts do *not* prove that blue sharks
do likewise. If, someday, as I intend, I can drift
about in mid-Atlantic for six months in a suitable
steamer and spend all calm days in excursions with
water glasses, glass-bottomed boats, and in helmet,
dangling, I will know far more about the ways of
sharks and other sea-folk than I do at present.

The mother blue shark measured nine feet, eight
inches in length and weighed a little over two hun-

181

dred and fifteen pounds. Readers avid for statistics
will welcome the news that each infant shark was
one-thirtieth of its parent's length, and as far as
weight is concerned it would require more than
twenty-two thousand, six hundred of the embryos
to balance the scales.

Although they were less than four inches over
all, they would have been born before many weeks.
Each was a perfect little shark — fins, snout,
mouth, all in place and nearly in proportion, while
the presence or absence of claspers indicated clearly
the sex. In the first ovary examined there were thirteen males and twelve females, showing how, even
in the lower forms of life, our sex is barely holding
its dominance!

The eye was the organ out of all proportion, and
as in the chick it showed that after birth sight would
be more important in escaping danger and securing
food than all other senses combined. To have one
last statistical fling; if sixteen of the embryo shark's
eyes were " laid end to end " they would reach from
its head to its tail, while in the parent eighty eyes
would be required for the same silly purpose. (But
this is all the fault of human language. I look at the
embryo and in a glance I sense the difference in
eyes, and my mind in an equally short space of time
supplies the probable reason, and I get my thrill
and it is over. But when I begin to rehash it all, and
tie it into awkward verbal knots, all spontaneity
seems gone. With all the advantages bequeathed
by inventors from Tegumai to Edison, there still

remains nothing comparable to first-hand seeing, hearing and touching.)

Another unusual character was the external gills. In the fullgrown shark five vertical slits behind the head are the sum total of visible gills. In the embryo there was a multitude of elongate, tentacle-fingers extending far outside the body. In the ovary these probably serve to absorb nourishment as well as any oxygen which may be available.

I once wrote somewhere that all sharks had sneering and terrifying expressions until you learned they were harmless and then you suddenly saw that they merely looked foolish and adenoidish. But the blue shark, both in life and death, has a much more pleasing and individual face. His look is of quiet wonder, and if one must carry an unchanging expression throughout life, I know of none better; it is dignified, fearless and indicates an interest in life, — and that is a happy combination.

To many of my experiences and specimens there is an aftermath of some kind. The sucking-fish and copepods had been described and labelled, catalogued and preserved in their respective little jars; the parent shark had, with etymological literalness, been drawn and quartered, photographed, measured and weighed, its skin and teeth preserved; the embryos had been cared for as only scientists can care for rare embryos. A week went by and as I passed one evening near the spot where the great jaws were put for safe keeping, I noticed a small glow. It was a dark night with no lunar or astral reflections and no glints came from the electric lights in the distant laboratory. Coming closer I looked and saw the jaws and teeth glowing eerily; the light was neither lambent, flickering nor twinkling — it was just a cold, colorless glow, the foxfire, the phosphorescence of bacteria, the bacteria which were aiding in the process of cleaning the cartilage and ivory. Again description palls, but it was very beautiful and quite unforgettable.

CHAPTER XII

IF WE live out our span of life on the earth without ever knowing a crab intimately we have missed having a jolly friendship. Life is a little incomplete if we can look back and recall these small people only as supplying the course after soup and with the Chablis. The ancient astrologers honored Cancer by making it one-twelfth of the celestial zodiac — the sign of the summer solstice; but to the majority of human beings crabs are merely creatures which skitter over the rocks, and, being rather unknown, are, therefore, to be exclaimed at and feared. Indeed they have even been branded with an opprobrious term in our language — *crabbed,* one who is sour-tempered and peevish.

Often I am asked, " What is a crab, anyhow? " and it is difficult to answer. We might say that it is a spider which lives in the sea, or a lobster which forever sits upon its folded tail or, to be Grecianly repetitious, we could call a crab a Brachyuran. The matter of the tail is of importance in much the same way that the short skirt is related to the old-fashioned crinoline. Lobsters are conservative old crustaceans, creeping along with half-extended bodies. When danger threatens, however, they be-

185

come suddenly galvanized into swift action. They forget their modesty and pick up their skirts to run, the long tail lashes forward, and they shoot backward into probable safety. The ancestors of the crab through all the long ages have gone the way of the bent tail, and kept it curled beneath them until it has diminished and passed from active use. This girding up of the tail end or telson, has left them balanced upon long active legs, their eyesight has improved tremendously, and to the ganglia of many has come an irresistible ambition for life elsewhere than in the water — the same ambition which once drove our ancestors out of the mud and slime into the clean air on the dry land.

When crabs have acquired our friendship we realize the possibility of becoming fond of the most outrageous creatures from Mars. For we soon come to overlook the structure of crabs, their outer facies, stalked eyes, numerous legs, their sidewise gait, the unyielding external skeleton, and in species and even individuals we perceive personality and a ridiculously manlike outlook on life. They are far and away the most human of all sea creatures. In addition to their very real cleverness in methods of attack, concealment, escape, and their quick recognition of friendly advances, there are two characteristics amazingly and comically anthropomorphic. Their eyes are on the ends of stalks yet they have a way of twisting and looking at us, or of peering out from their shallow trenches precisely as a person looks out from half-closed lids.

TWO CITIZEN CRABS OF NONSUCH

Most convincingly human is the pair of claw legs not used for locomotion, but as in ourselves, acting as arms, hands, and fingers, which in a multitude of ways simulate the movements and functions of our own upper limbs.

On Nonsuch Island, Bermuda, and in the waters round about, there are quite fifty species of crabs. Each has its particular niche in life and fills it to the best of its ability, but only a bare half-dozen stand out with any distinctness to our human vision and imagination. Once crabs had become crabs there seemed to be no limit to their evolution — to the niches into which they could successfully mold themselves. It was like the gift of flight to insects, of song to birds, and of brain to man. Just as every individual Babbitt is a relative success in his own small, particular field, so we might reverse our glasses and see worthy accomplishment in every species of crab. But let us rather sweep the field with a coarse net and see what comes up, and select only those exceptional ones which catch the eye at first glance.

The original home of all crabs (and for that matter of all human beings) is the sea, and today there are tiny crabs which spend their lives floating and swimming on the surface hundreds of miles out at sea, and there are giants with a ten-foot spread of legs which stalk about in utter darkness on the bottom of the abyssal depths. Nonsuch crabs show every extreme phase of life. In the water there are Floaters, Swimmers, and Bottom Walkers; on land there are Cliff Dwellers, Sand Livers, Nomad Hill-men, and Homesteaders.

I once saw men in shell-holes menaced by a flock of swooping, peering planes, by a deadly horizontal stratum of machine-gun bullets a yard above the ground, and worst of all, as dusk closed down, by the ghastly Very lights which seem to pierce to one's soul. Their only hope of life was to look more like bits of the shell-hole than the shell-hole itself. I re-called this in the middle of the Sargassum Sea, over a thousand miles from any dry land, when I used to scoop up on deck netfuls of the golden weed, ap-parently a pure culture of algæ, to see it produce, like a conjurer's rabbits from a hat, a score of little animals of a half-dozen wholly unrelated groups who had made this weed their permanent shell-hole of life. In form, color, pattern, and even in motion they were botanized; algæ — bits of the sargassum — angular, golden, mottled, and with a weaving, bending movement as of seaweed rocked by the waves.

Most abundant was a small crab, a chunky, four-square chap, hardly a half-inch across, who but for the grace of eyes, mouth, muscles, and ganglia might have been a stray torn shred of gulfweed. This was my first introduction to the well-named Little Wanderer of the Sargassum — *Planes mi-nutus.*

Planes has played a part in history — all un-knowingly. Christopher Columbus was a great man but no carcinologist, and in the dark, discouraged days when his crew began to murmur and demand to be allowed to turn homewards, the discovery of crabs among the passing weed perhaps carried more weight than we know. More scientific men than Columbus would have thought that weed-inhabiting crabs must be indicative of adjacent shores.

Bermuda is not at the very center of the Sargassum Sea but it is close to it, and so it is to be expected that day after day, golden patches or fields of the weed drift past, or are blown upon the beaches of Nonsuch. Here, untold hosts of the little wandering crabs find their nemesis. The fish, the big swimming crabs, and even the slow-moving shell-less snails seem to sense the approach of disaster, and desert the masses of weed as they drift shoreward. But *Planes* are loyal to the last, and every windrow of weed thrown up on the sand shelters dozens of them. They live on for a time with no hope, for when their floating home is again launched by a high tide, it is dead, and sinks at once. And on the shore, birds of all kinds gather and some, like the turnstones, have learned to push and roll the weed over and over, butting it with their heads, so that the sanctuary of untold generations of crabs becomes useless.

There is a bond between the weed and the crab, more ancient than the similarity in color and pattern. While the Sargassum Sea is now a going concern, made up (according to a recent estimate) of not less than twenty million tons of weed, this seaweed differs from most algæ by having no roots and developing no spores or organs of reproduction. It exists, then, by an endless growth, a perpetual increase of leaves and air-filled floats. But no matter for how many centuries this has been going on, there is no doubt but that the first weed was torn by storms from the rocks and reefs of the West Indies, and swept by wind and currents out into the great dead center of two and a half million square miles over which it is scattered today. So the floating vegetation originally was a rock grower.

While the Wanderer Crab spends its life far from land, sighting it only by accident, yet it, too, is not a swimmer by blood, for all its ancestors and many of its living relatives are Cliff Dwellers such as the scarlet *Grapsus*. But it has long since exchanged mineral for vegetable protection. A lumberman might be most expert in riding logs down a series of rapids, but he would cut a poor figure and would soon lose his life competing with a Swiss mountain climber. So although the Sargassum crab may be stranded at the very foot of rocks over which his cousins are scampering, he can only hold tight to the last to his bit of weed.

When we come to examine *Planes* more closely we find an exquisite adjustment to the exigencies of his life. As soon as a fish begins to become less conservative and starts climbing among the fronds of algæ or creeping along the bottom or even clambering out upon the shore, his fins begin to suffer. But somewhere between the climbing out and the tearing of the webs Nature steps in and in her deliberate and mysterious manner remolds the webs into palms and the rays into fingers, and the mental adjustment to the new habit and habitat is consolidated by the all-important physical one. *Planes'* ancestors as Cliff Dwellers needed only thin legs and ankles, and *Planes* as a Weed Climber would hardly need any radical change, no more than a rock-living baboon would require among swaying, yielding branches. But when one's whole material world is afloat, and subject to constant buffeting and upsetting by waves it would go hard with the first crab fitted with mountain-climbing legs when hurled off his vegetable raft. On the other hand if Nature had done the obvious thing and provided him with broad, spatulate, oarlike swimming legs, he would be as much at home in the interstices of the weed as a bat in a tangled thicket, or spaghetti on a spoon.

We find a clever compromise. The posterior legs of *Planes* are very slightly flattened, muscle being hardly needed in traversing weed under water. Four fathoms down I can pull myself through coral branches with a crooked finger, whereas in a tree, both hands and feet are necessary for progress. And along the anterior surface of each of the limbs of *Planes* is a broad, bladelike row of feather hairs, slender stems like pliable spun glass with innumerable short barbs, interlocking, yet lying down at a touch when pressed endwise. They offer no resistance when their owner is creeping through the tangled foliage, but when a sudden wave projects

191

him into mid-ocean with two miles of water beneath and ravenous fish in the middle distance, he strikes out, and more skillfully than any man-driven, eight-oared barge, *Planes* rows swiftly up and back to sanctuary, feathering his oars (*mea culpa*) as he goes.

Some of the Wanderer Crabs we collect are small, others have attained the full adult stature of three-fourths of an inch; structurally all are as alike as one and fifty shadows. In color and pattern, however, they allow no chance of accumulated memory in their enemies. A fish may nose out one *Planes,* but none of the half dozen left in the same patch of weed bears any close resemblance to its dead brother, so each much be detected or passed by on the merits or demerits of its own particular weed resemblance. *Planes* can have a background suiting of pale yellow green or orange or dark brown or olive green, and his squarish little back can be slightly mottled, or etched with an infinity of brown and yellow patterns. There may be transverse lines over the eyes, with dim rectangles or squares or triangles on mid-back; some have ikon-like traceries, or tapestry palimpsests — scores of patterns, any one of which would suffice for a crab with a less kaleidoscopic habitat. Just when we smugly feel that we appreciate to the full this variety of tint and hue, and concede a rather condescending approval of its function, we come across a little *Planes* with an oblong of glistening frost — a milky white blob of enamel laid across his shoulders.

192

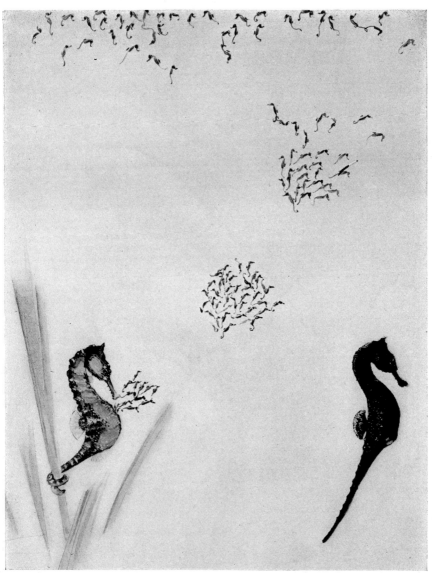

Painting by Else Bostelmann.

43. The birth of three hundred young Seahorses, and the change in color of the father's armor on the following day.

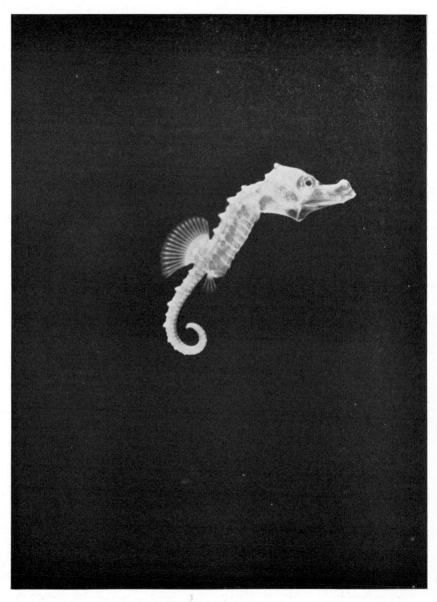

44. Young Seahorse twenty minutes old.

TWO CITIZEN CRABS OF NONSUCH

In the hand or under our lens this spells conspicuousness and sets our placid theories at naught, until examination of the first sargassum branch which comes to hand reveals the irregular but very abundant spots of the white, crystalline homes of bryozoa or moss-animals which encrust the floats and fronds. Our shell-hole mimics are outdoing themselves. I collect a hundred crabs and find that about fifty are pretending to be bryozoans as well as weed. This resemblance tells us another fact — that moss animals inhabited sargassum weed ages before *Planes* came on the scene.

Just as a glistening mirror eclipses its frame, so in the white-spotted crabs we forget not only the mottlings of color and the pattern, but even the outline of the crab fades from optical dominance and we see only square, rounded, oval, rectangular, double or dumb-bell-shaped white spots. Under water another resemblance leaps to the eye — the ever-ready banks of swimming feather-blades bear a most perfect resemblance to occasional masses of hydroids, those mothers and daughters of jellyfish, whose slender little palm-tree oases sprout from the edges of the fronds.

Of the doings and adventures, dangers and joys of the Wanderer Crabs in their home in open ocean none may write. A biographical diary of *Planes* would surely be an epic. In early July I found numerous females with large masses of eggs held safe beneath the abdomen, and when I came to examine them closely there was the imprint of sar-

193

gassum sanctuary etched upon the little crabs even before birth. Some of the wriggling embryos were straw yellow, others orange, others dark olive. The eyes were most conspicuous and invariably dark sepia brown, their relatively great size showing how important they must be to the new-hatched larvæ. The newly deposited spawn is always bright orange and when we press back the little circular disk of the crab's abdomen, it looks like a delicately fashioned plate heaped high with a pile of diminutive cumquats. Each egg is only a fiftieth of an inch in diameter, but in the exquisite machinery of development it is perfection, while in value to the coming generation of Wanderer Crabs its diameter is that of the Earth itself.

I have never seen the first or zoëa or " life " stage, but it is doubtless the usual giant-headed, spiny, long-tailed changeling which is the childhood of most crabs. This is the most critical time in all the growth of the Wanderer, for zoëa is a swimming animal, and as man in his extreme youth is a quadruped and creeps about the floor on hands and knees, so crabs when they leave the egg revert to swimming ancestors. In a single branch of gulfweed as large as a man's head I have found six crabs with eggs, and as the average number of eggs is about six hundred, there would in time be thirty-six hundred zoëas swimming busily about. In spite of spines these bits of natatory life are toothsome morsels for any enemy of size, and it is probably a fortunate brood which numbers a half dozen survivors at the time of the last moult. This, in technical parlance, is the megalops stage, and it always seems to me to correspond to the gawky period of youth, when by length of trousers, hands in pockets and a very disagreeable cigar the boy attempts to attain his idea of manhood.

Megalops has forever put behind him his infancy swims. Of equal value with his eyes is the cloak of invisibility which will lead many deadly enemies to pass him by, and in this youthful stage of development we see already well-established, the beginnings of the mottlings, marblings, and the pale enamel of the crab to come. His joy and pride must be his bare limbs, still free from the feather-blades of the adult, and his amazing claws which are long, curved, and sharp-toothed like his pincers. There is no doubt that the god of crabs intends to conserve his remnant of a half dozen. It would need a hurricane to dislodge this youngster when once he has taken hold upon the weed. Like a stubborn, adolescent mustache which exists chiefly in the imagination of its owner, the elongated abdomen must be a continual worry to Megalops. He strives to keep it bent and curled under, but it is constantly slipping and flattening into a hateful, lobsterine straightness. One more moult and the carapace widens to full shield-shape, the claws are reduced, the feather-blades appear, and the unmistakable crab insignia — the concealed abdomen — becomes an accomplished fact. The biblical parable is reversed in the case of these crabs: those which founded their homes upon

NONSUCH

rocks are confined to the narrow insular borders of the tropics, while our *Planes,* whose home is infinitely less enduring than sand, live abundantly from Nova Scotia to the Straits of Magellan, and from California to New Zealand. It is one of the most successful crabs in the world, and, like the hoatzin of neotropical river banks, as long as its unique haunts continue, its race is safe from extinction.

Nevertheless, when fate drives *Planes* and his particular bit of material cosmos ashore on Nonsuch, then nemesis closes down. No prayers to great Cancer high overhead in the heavens will avail. Day by day as the foliage blackens, his livery of mottled gold becomes more conspicuous; as the fronds dry, his gills ache for the flowing salt, and sooner or later on his trips into the water and back he is seen by hostile bird or crab or fish, or, stricken by the alien air and sand, he sinks down, slain by the inconceivably slight chance of having been cast upon the only bit of dry land in all the expanse of millions of miles of kindly, weed-strewn ocean.

As I write, sitting in my laboratory nearly one hundred feet above the sea on my little outlying Bermuda Island of Nonsuch, a land crab has climbed the rough wall and is clinging half-way to the ceiling. At odd moments I have tried to fathom this unreasonable exhibition of Excelsiorism, but have failed utterly.

The most reasonable explanation is that it corresponds to a dog turning around several times

before he lies down, or the matutinal, utterly inef-
fective wing-flapping of the domestic rooster before
crowing. At a certain season of the year, our purple
land crabs are troubled with an ancestral memory of
the necessity of leaving the sea and reascending to
the highest possible points of safety. And here on
Nonsuch there is a single annual impulse, irresistible on the part of females whose breeding season
has just passed, to climb trees, porches, buildings,
roofs, even chimneys. There they remain with just
about as much reason as human tree-roosting record
seekers, until they are blown down, or become tired,
or the ancestral instinct loses its grip.

As a matter of fact one might remain for many
weeks on Nonsuch without seeing one of these land
crabs which are among the island's most numerous
inhabitants. Only the multitude of holes indicates
that there is a race of mysterious troglodytes in-
habiting every diggable square yard. A combination of rain and warmth seems to be the open
sesame, and one day in early spring word passes
around by some method more mysterious than wireless, and at the entrance of hundreds of holes can
be seen a glint of scarlet. For a few days the crabs
are shy and pop in and out of their tunnels as I
go by.

Then simultaneously fear passes from all the
crabs and in the shade of the cedars, scores of the
jolly little chaps scramble about. Pigmentally they
are most artistic additions to the dark green of their
background, for their bodies are tinted with warm

orange and yellow, set off by a cape of rich plum
color, shading into purplish black, the legs being
bright red. They dig deep for succulent grass roots
and spend much of their time pulling off the stems
and mumbling the broken ends like children with
all-day-suckers. They are comical enough at best,
but when a crab holds a straw in one of his claws
and sucks vigorously at it, all he needs is a country
store and a bottle of pop in front of him to personify utter rural idleness. They sometimes pull at
a grass stem so hard that when it gives way unexpectedly they tumble over backwards. After one
such accident I saw a neighboring male rush at his
companion, but the other was up and on guard in
an instant. Both threatened with a movement curi-
ously like the preparatory weaving of a boxer's
arms — it was the upward feint of a fiddler crab
executed circularly.

I cut off the retreat of one of these crabs as I
walked along a cedar-lined path. For a moment he
stood his ground and from a two-inch height he
threatened me with waving claws. But I defied him
and placed my foot over his hole. Only one trick of
escape remained — to sidle beneath a patch of grass
and try to become a bit of parti-colored shadow. I
closed down on him and held both claws helpless
between finger and thumb. Like Humpty Dumpty,
he has a cephalothorax, that is, his head is merged
immovably into his shoulders and body. He could
not turn his neck and look at me, but Nature plays
fair, and he cocked up his periscope eyes and

twiddled them inquiringly. At a touch they swiveled down into ready-made troughs, all lined with a circle of stiff eyewinkers or sweepers which, like our own, clear the eye of sand or other débris. With us, however, a proper eyelid slips down and over the eye. In the case of my captive the entire crab became momentarily the eyelid and winker and moved up over the eye.

For a minute my crab was motionless, then with a mighty twist he somersaulted backward into freedom, leaving both great claws in my hand. His second line of defense was played; he had relinquished his weapons to lighten his flight. Knowing that in the end I should set him free, I was merciless now and pounced upon him before he could scuttle into his hole. I had nothing more to fear from his pincers and turned him over and over, examining every detail of his armor, while he lay motionless, shamed by the theft of his sword and lance. Finally I raised the infolded abdomen. This is a crab's most vital of vital spots and when he felt his most vulnerable organs exposed he called upon a third, and last, and wholly unexpected resource. From out of some concealed gland there poured a black liquor, such as locusts distill, but before it could spread, or drop down, he began to send a stream of air into it and it rose and rose, and from black became sepia, then pale brown, then an iridescent tan reflecting every hue of the spectrum. Still it increased until the whole crab and my finger were wholly concealed beneath a sphere of golden bubbles. I touched my tongue to it and detected an unpleasant, acrid taste, and I knew that if I were an enemy of lesser stature, with a more perfect sense of taste or smell than we mortal men possess, I should have been unable to devour him, and should probably have dropped him at once.

I pretended I was all that, and placed him gently near his hole. He side-tracked to the entrance, then turned, raised both eyes to the utmost height and wriggled the low stumps of the vanished arms and claws which rested safely in my pocket. It recalled the forever unknown gesture of the missing arm of the gladiator's torso, and I could but wonder whether that of the crab was intended to be one of final defiance or a salute of gratitude before he slipped slowly from my sight. I well knew that any sympathy would be wasted upon my armless victim. I examined the stumps and found them dry and already shriveled. At this very moment strange internal forces had begun work in the crab, carrying infinitesimal tissue material, and in the course of the coming few weeks new claws would sprout. No plan or blue-print was needed. In the orderly alchemy of the crab's blood, cell would be placed inevitably upon cell, none wasted, none awry. Finally he would be ready again to face me should I pass that way, with his armor intact, ready again with all his little plays for life.

We have only our own human race to blame if we endow our land crab with considerable conceit. I do not intend low puns when I emphasize the fact that

45. Silversides.

46. Tooth of Tiger Shark.
Enlarged seven times.

TWO CITIZEN CRABS OF NONSUCH

Gecarcinus lateralis is a climber and has won a place above the salt. Let us think of her early on a summer morning curled tightly in the small chamber at the end of her burrow. It is pitch dark, but these small people of the earth have not yet deadened their perceptions so that they have to renew the youth of their senses by means of wires or wireless, bells and clocks. That is our prerogative.

So somehow she knows it is dawn, and, as she is not nearly as nocturnal as she is thought to be, she scrambles sideways the three or four feet to the sharp upward bend, and then up to the outer world. The entrance is at the edge of a fifty-foot cliff, and she can look down on the old ocean, just as the wife of a successful Italian contractor might drive down from Fifth Avenue and look with lorgnette at Mott or Pell Street. She probably cannot hear the songs of the little vireos or detect the scarlet and yellow of the goldfinches looping past, but if she knew what conceit was she could feel certain that she was a member of the terrestrial, air-breathing FFN. But as so often happens to those not to the manor born, at critical moments a slip occurs, the horns and hoofs are for a second's fraction exposed; so even with land crabs there is a price to pay. Nature has decreed that for a race of creatures to be worthy of such drastic progress, the young may not be born to all the shelter and ease to which its parents have won, but must, at least to a slight degree, go through the motions of the transition from water to air. The salamander

201

has its newt, the frog its tadpole, and the land crab has its aquatic zoëa.

Fate had planned through all the eons of life on the earth, since the land crab's ancestors and my own were one, that on this day of this year I should reach the entrance of the tunnel at the exact moment of her emergence. From the date of our common ancestor this would doubtless be something like B.C. 999,998.070 plus, as we artlessly reckon time. A.D. 1931. At any rate here we were face to face, and I saw at a glance that this was not only a large, brilliantly marked land crab, but that a great mass of eggs was guarded beneath the absurdly small tail flap. My own especial ancestors had left the ancient watery medium eons of years before those of my crab, and so I was much more at home on land than she; also I had gained in stature and in cephalic ganglion content. So I pitted my activity and cunning against hers and won. Then I carried her gently to my laboratory and installed her in an aquarium upon several inches of earth and sand, and in the corner I placed a small dish of fresh water. In the latter action I made a mistake. I cannot keep in mind the almost utter lack of natural fresh water receptacles on Nonsuch, and when I offered Her Crabship fresh water it was the unconscious gesture of one terrestrial being to another.

At midnight I bethought me of my lady land crab and visited the aquarium. There was no sign of her for she had dug herself a tunnel, descended it and somehow closed it after her. The water in the dish had been the irresistible stimulus at the critical moment — every egg had been deposited in it and the great majority of embryos had felt the ancestral demand for this fluid and had burst their bonds — the soft egg tissues lying limp and torn. Out the youngsters had come, full of that hope and vigor which we, through our last one thousand generations of ease and over-comforts, possess only in a pale diluted amount. The liquid was of the right temperature and consistency, but some vital thing was lacking, and after a few futile kicks and leaps all had succumbed and settled to the bottom, dead. This marked another bond between the little crabs and ourselves, for immeasurably removed from the old watery life as we are, yet if the humors of our eye have run out or we have lost much blood, a skillful surgeon can replace our optical or our life fluids with salt water which in time will be absorbed and replaced. If fresh water be used it is poison, and blindness or death may result.

All the litter of purple land crabs perished, and I felt very sad. So primed were the little chaps for instant reaction to liquid of any kind, that of a dozen eggs taken from the parent and placed in formalin, eight hatched into perfect zoëas within the first three minutes, before the toxicity could be felt.

CHAPTER XIII

I CLEARED my laboratory table of the most pressing messes, and seeing no immediate squall in prospect out at sea, I started for the Nonsuch tidepools. My artist called to me for criticism of a colored plate of snail drawings. She had just completed the delineation of one of the most beautiful things in the world, but one which, like sunshine and peacocks, has become æsthetically oxidized in our minds through over-familiarity. I suppose if rainbows were never absent from sunsets, and our groves were filled with morpho butterflies, we would begin to appreciate the soft hues of moths and the hundred marvellous greys of clouds.

I returned to the laboratory and compared the painting with the subject. I found nothing to criticize about the first — there was Snail, both in and out of his house, as true as life. Then I looked at the little creature himself and I forgot about the tidepools. He was in a glass dish, and I transported both snail and myself to a place where the outside world does not dare to bother — my own private Nonsuch den — and my diminutive shellfish and myself looked at each other eye to eye.

It struck me at once how perfectly silly it would

204

be to call human beings " white-oaks," for no man is an oak and only a certain proportion are white. But it is equally illogical to indicate snails and oysters and octopuses by the term " shellfish " for none of them are fish and many have no shells. However we cannot give up " starfish " or " crayfish " and editors have an unreasonable objection to newly coined words. Mollusk is really the best general name, for all shellfish are soft. Whichever way we look at it, the English language is very often scant when we require exactness.

My snail was a periwinkle, or winkle as they called him in the days of Good King Wenceslas, and of gastronomic King Hal as well, for dozens of generations of humans have proved hundreds of generations of winkles palatable. How winkle came first to Bermuda no one knows, but he has followed the ships of men from England to New York and elsewhere and by one of the one thousand accidents has made Nonsuch his home. With his fellow countryfolk — the house sparrows — he has thrived and is found occasionally with other shells on the rocks.

At present he was quiet and conservative — deep within his shell with his door shut tight — thinking the periwinklish thoughts which one does when deep within one's shell. I filled his dish with salt water, and however tight his brown mahogany swirl of a door seemed to be, yet knowledge of the change in the outer element somehow trickled through. The lid lifted — a dark finger of a tentacle wavered

205

tentatively, an eye glinted in the portico and out came the owner. His ancestors, like mine, unquestionably came from the sea, but his scientific godfathers for once have christened him reasonably and he is *Littorina litorea* — alliteratively and redoubled — a Shore of the Shore creature.

The little helix was now gliding across my tabletop — a wisp of twisted lime and a pinch of soft flesh, typifying all the strange personality of his race. He was a young periwinkle — not fully adult, and, like myself, representative of the last, the most recent generation.

Shortening the level of my outlook to his, little by little I began to see existence from the eye of a snail. I forgot the common bonds between our phyla — gastronomic, utilitarian, financial, even artistic, and took sheer joy in watching him, trying to pry as deep as I possibly could into his molluscan soul.

Life seemed full of purpose to him — a life that, without interruption extended back to the first snail. This is a truism, applicable to all other living organisms, and far back in the dim early ages of earth life, there lived some creature which, today, snail and I can call *our* ancestor. But the changes which intervened in the meantime are immeasurably divergent. As my line stretches back my brain contracts, my muscles expand, I drop down on all fours, sprout a tail, develop long ears and snout, my teeth simplify and insects satisfy my hunger; reptilian characters accrue, my ribs increase; I slip into the water, and looking for the last time upon

the land, I sink beneath the surface. Gills mark
my rhythm of breath, limbs shrink to fins, and even
these vanish, while my backbone, last hold upon
the higher life, dissolves to a notochord. At one end
of my evolution Roosevelt called me friend — millions of years earlier any passing worm might have
hailed me as brother.

My little periwinkle has glided about unchanged
through all the ages — through the travails of
primitive apeman, the frightened, nocturnal scur-
ryings of tiny insect-eaters, the splashing of mud-
hopping amphibians, the swimming of swift-finned,
water creatures, and the wriggling of still more
lowly ancestors of the sea. When a nation shuts itself off from other nations behind physical barriers
or those of conceit, progress in the best sense ceases;
when an individual miser or hermit or egoist lives
safe and selfishly, he becomes automatically static.
Finally when a race of creatures develops an ability
to clothe itself in impregnable marble palaces, im-
mune to a host of dangers which threaten less ar-
mored brethren, there is little need of their changing to meet new conditions.

And so let us compare the past history of man
and his mammalian forebears who have fought the
fight naked, with the line of gentle, sheltered snails.
Ten thousand years have seen the development of
what we are pleased to call civilization; ten million
years ago man began to be man rather than ape;
fifty millions of years saw the first mammals that
ever were. Five times this time, or two hundred and

fifty million years before 1931, saw genera of snails living and thriving, unchanged from these alive to-day — at a time when no bird or mammal or flowering plant had yet appeared. In the Upper Cambrian mollusks were abundant, and a few well-developed and going snails were living in the Lower Cambrian — five hundred million years back. Now look at our periwinkle with renewed respect; his ancestors, with shell, muscles, movement and life closely similar to his, were alive when the earth itself was only three-quarters evolved.

We are reasonably certain that the higher evolution had little impetus in the deep sea; conditions there were too stable and unchanging, competition was hardly felt: Not until the hard rock and the shifting sands of the shore were encountered, the crash and drag of waves, the submersion and exposure of varying tides, enemies in pool and air — these demanded change, adaptation, extermination, and progress.

As yet we know nothing definitely about the very early ancestors of our snail, but as we have seen, even in the early eons of the sea he had achieved a shell, and when he crawled shoreward and out upon primeval mud-flats, it was as if he dragged with him a bit of the unchanging deeps. As long as food was at hand and no danger threatened he crept slowly along, peering safely from a narrow crevice between earth and shell, and at the first hint of trouble withdrew within his mineral castle. Such a procedure made for individual safety, but cramped the style of progress. In the course of time the architecture might vary — spines and pillars, furrows and cones might be added, pigment of the whole spectrum, a hut-like home which was its own door, or an elaborate hinged entrance; a mere flattened scale or an embossed superstructure of jointed armor — to such unimportant lengths of variation, but no farther, might a mollusk go without endangering precedent. No wonder we find these creatures dominant as fossils, when in life they are little else, born in a ready-made, rocky sarcophagus, with interior decoration and reinforced concrete construction as their chief indoor sports throughout life.

With the slogan of " eternally conservative " the ancient snails spread along all the shores of the sea, clambering to the furthest spray of high tide. While they were content to munch old fragments of algæ and cringe to all the cosmos, their neighbors fought and died, and through their changed offspring lived again. Landward crept the pioneers, fish, crabs, worms, and even lowly single-cellers, all changing, altering every portion of their beings to meet and cope with the new conditions. And along with this host, quietly glided the same old snails, outstripping their other neighbors of the dawn of life — sponges, jelly-fish, and sea-urchins — which were fated forever to remain prisoners of the denser medium, and hastening in the footsteps of their betters. Today I see cousins of the periwinkle in full sunlight, creeping upon dry leaves high over my head, far from their original home, yet with almost no external adjustments to the new life. If sheer number of species spells success, the mollusks are second only to insects, with at least sixty thousand of living forms.

Having abused my little Helix and heaped scorn upon his ancestors and his conservatism, it amuses me to think of some of his virtues and achievements. " Just a snail " is the sum total of the conscious thought given by most of us to these creatures. Even when we become enthusiastic over the delicacy of form and color of a collection of shells, we think of them rather as an assemblage of inorganic crystals than as the homes of living individual animals, which have sought food and a mate, have travelled perhaps many miles in their lifetime, and experienced adventures as momentous to them as shipwreck or a creeping barrage to us.

The shells of mollusks are as worthy of attention as they are beautiful. The interests of a Wall Street banker and a collector of sea-shells might reasonably be taken as representing antithetical extremes, and yet shells from the point of view of money have vitally concerned both the savage and the man of science. The latter has been willing to pay hundreds of dollars for a unique or an especially rare specimen, while for centuries cowries and wampum have passed as the only monetary medium of exchange in many lands. To be sure four thousand cowries have sometimes had only the value of a shilling, but on the other hand, in China I have had to load a pony with strings of strung cash, so great was their weight. And wampum of the right purple color once had great purchasing power in land and slaves.

While our sophisticated banker might sneer at the idea of a cabinet of shells, however beautiful or rare, and laugh at a necklace of cowries hung on some savage squaw, yet he will pay fabulous sums for the shining spheres which are the evidences of disease in four and twenty pearl oysters. And again, in the case of pukka oysters our man of the city thrills with the satisfaction and approval of a conchologist though only for a brief time between cocktails and soup, and gustatorily rather than intelligently.

All the time we are rambling on with what we are pleased to imagine worthy lucubrations, our periwinkle is steadily placing the inches behind him. He turns neither to right nor left, and his pace is unchanged whether over glass, cedar, blotting paper, or manuscript. At the edge of the table I turn him into reverse, and he unconsciously glides back — the points of the compass are all one to him. I start him again at the bottom of his dish and watch him carefully through the glass. When his operculum or lid is slowly lowered from place it is followed by his head — a real one with mouth, two sensitive horns or tentacles and two bright eyes at the base of the horns. The only other part of the snail which is visible is the oval, flat, fleshy foot on which he moves. There is a line down the center and the periwinkle advances by shoving ahead first the right then left side just as a man shuffles along on skis or snowshoes, only the snail gains distance by successive waves or ripples. The horns look and move exactly like the trunk of an elephant, the eyes look like black dots, the head is dark brown and the body and foot are pale olive green: — this is Periwinkle as I see him.

When he reaches the freshly written preceding paragraph, he smudges a line of the inky writing as he passes over it — as if he well knew how much better it should have been written. In fact when I come to examine his trail I find a split infinitive quite rightly smeared with his slime. The smudge is made by a fluid which he pours out in front, thus oiling his path in advance, smoothing the boulders of dust and killing any unpleasant feel or taste of inks and other alien fluids in his way. I think I have heard of sledges in Madeira, which ease their passage over dry cobbles with dripping oil, or it is as if a sleigh were provided with a pair of ice machines in the fore runners. It is an excellent idea and brings a snail clean and fresh to the end of its journey, whereas otherwise it would be coated and choked with dust.

As Periwinkle climbs the algæ-coated glass he leaves another trail — a narrow, cleared path on the glass over which his mouth passes and which his tongue scrapes clean. And I marvel again at the slimy alchemy by which he can transmute lowly vegetable scum and salt water into graceful limestone spirals and strata of mother-of-pearl.

SNAIL FOLK

I now begin my detective work, which is all that real science consists of, and first of all hold a stop watch on my periwinkle. I know that I am only imitating Aesop, but in the famous Reptile-Rodent Derby no exact time was given. I find that on the straightaway, Snail can make three inches in one minute, and several heats of this one (which I have rather obviously called James) and of a brother snail, give the same pace. To show off my mathematical skill I may state that this speed will in the course of time and space give a foot in four minutes, a yard in twelve and a mile in about fifteen days. Having named my periwinkle and had his portrait painted, his life is inviolate, so I sacrifice a neighbor of exactly the same size. After a painless death I remove him from his shell and find that he weighs one and a quarter grams, his house two grams and his thin, horny operculum only seven-thousandths of a gram. We have a corresponding figure in a man weighing one hundred and twenty-five pounds, carrying a shed of two hundred pounds and a door of about a pound weight.

One of the most amazing things in the world and one of the most exquisite adjustments is the gradual unconscious fashioning of the shell by constant additions to the rim as the inmate slowly increases in size. No blueprints, no architects' designs, no plans; just a formless mass of living jelly taking lime dissolved in the water and depositing it in smooth nacre, or twists and columns and ridges; dyeing it scarlet, lavender, green and royal purple. The color

213

NONSUCH

factory is along the very rim of the head, so when an accident occurs to the shell farther back, while the marble patch is laid on at once, it is always white, uncolored.

The shellfish which have ensconced themselves in their armor just where the sea pounds heaviest have a double defense which seems well-nigh impregnable. Yet one of the most dramatic things is the way other organisms have learned to encompass the smashing power of their watery moats, and to pierce their marble forts. It is a fight against strong odds and has several fascinating twists. Two families of the snails of Nonsuch which live their lives in tidepools or on the cliffs amid swirling currents or within crash of the breakers, are the limpets and the chitons.

If we do not mind returning for a few minutes to this damp, agitated ancestral home of ours; and squat down among the water-worn gorges and canyons, we will see here and there the little wigwam-like dwellings of the limpets. The low, spreading, well-guyed tents of the Arabs are the only structures which will stand the terrific blasts of the desert storms — and in this snail world of crashing, pounding elements, block houses, turrets and towers would soon be torn to fragments. But even in this narrow, dynamic zone Nature has exquisitely exact adaptations. Low down, where for ten out of the twelve hours of tidal change there is no quiet or rest, the limpets are few in number, but these daring pioneers are encased in low, very stout shell-

214

tents, with smooth slopes on all sides. As we get higher, the shells become thinner, and well out of the watery rush of mid-tide we even find decorative furrows and ridges and a bit of color — a dash of pigment here and there. What lessons the designers of suburban bungalows could learn from the so-called lower animals!

If we watch closely we will find another equally delicate adjustment to this life among inimical elements — this time a habit. Where we are sitting, drenched with spray, but beyond the actual impact of the breakers, we observe that the limpets are creeping slowly over the uneven surface — our cracks their canyons, our irregularities their ranges of mountains. They have no definite route but feed as they go, scraping the new growth of algæ from the surface.

Armed with water goggles so that we can see more clearly, and, crab-like, clinging tightly with hands and feet (and longing for a tail), we creep down into the front line trenches of this elemental battle-field. Here the waves threaten to tear away our unshelled molluscan forms and roll us down the submerged slope of Bermuda mountain. Gasping, and with eyes concentrated for the brief intervals between the crash of the green and white water, we detect the limpets of this zone. None are moving, all are quiescent, and if we choose one or two for intensive observation we see that their resting place is perfectly adapted to the outline of their shells. With a knife we pry one loose and

215

find it is actually sunken in a shallow pit — another guard against being swept out to sea. This implies a permanent residence of sorts and then we remember that Aristotle, two thousand years ago, knew and wrote about the daily grazing excursions of the limpets. When the pounding of the waves eases somewhat, they leave their forms and hastily crawl about, swinging their tiny many-toothed scythe, and cutting a swath through the seaweed fields as they go; then they return, how, we do not know; whether by retracing their glairy trail, or by the dim remembrance of crags and valleys, or by some strange memory of place, a homing quality of the little snail's ganglion.

The simplicity of the outward appearance of the limpet's tent is deceiving, for it belongs to the helices or twisted spirals and its young show distinct coils. Associated with the limpets, on the same rocks, are chitons or armadillo snails which have eight, hard, transverse plates in a line, as unlike an ordinary snail as may be. They cling tightly, and when pried off, curl up like a pill-bug, or an armadillo. In my brief résumé of devolution I have said there was a time when my ancestors had many more ribs than I, and this repetition of similar parts is an almost certain sign of lowness of type. The chitons are the only snails with more than one shell; they have eight, and all quite untwisted, in a straight line like the snails of the precambrian days.

Here then we have mussels, periwinkles, limpets and chitons, all living close to the shore, all pro-

216

tected with hard shells from danger, all vegetarians. The rocks should be covered with untold hosts of them, as safe in the battle of life as a knight in full armor would be in an encounter with half a dozen serfs.

But the law of compensation is always at work, and there can be no aces up the sleeve in the game with Nature. The stakes are Life or Death and too often the dice seem loaded in favor of Mung. Here is an unusually large, strong limpet. His vacuum grip defies the smash of waves; his constitution can withstand the occasional drenchings and submersions of fresh rain water; his gills hold sufficient store of salt water to last through prolonged heat droughts. Yet one day, without warning, there occurs whatever, in limpet language, stands for explosion, eruption, tornado, cyclone — his house is ripped from its foundation, he disappears down a great throat, and he is troubled no more by the self-sufficient smugness of too great success: And the oystercatcher, the great black and white bird, wipes her scarlet, knifelike beak on the nearest rock, and trots unconcernedly on to the next limpet or mussel or chiton. Any sympathy for the snail is leavened by thoughts of the untold generations of oyster-catchers during which the shape, pattern, thinness, sharpness, verticalness of their beak blades have developed hand in hand with habit and skill. Admiration of a specialist in attack must always exceed concern for the safety of a pacifist.

One more action and reaction in the life of a

limpet or a mussel and we will leave the world of snails. Again please visualize a limpet which has attained adult snailhood unharmed by elements or waterfowl. He is crouched in his perfect fitting form, perhaps peering out through the merest crack at his two-plane world, when he feels the touch of a tentacle on his shell. Instantly he draws tightly down and does everything which a limpet does in the way of bolts, bars, portcullis, blinds and vizors. Still his sensitive shell transmits the shifting play of a delicate touch. Then a heavy weight presses down, and for a time nothing more happens. One of the most terrible sounds in the world is the sudden, unexpected grating of the keel of a boat upon hidden rocks, and some similar sound comes to the ears, or along the nerves of the limpet. Grind, grind, grind, comes the new sound — we might liken it to an endless filing or scraping of sandpaper.

By virtue of our capacity as onlooker, we shift attention from the intimate emotions of our limpet to his environment. A great snail — the moon-snail — with a rounded shell and a large amount of fleshy foot has climbed upon the tent-roof and is busy with some nefarious work. We perceive a whole kit of tools — burglars' or executioners', or what you will. A narrow band covered with thousands of minute sharp teeth, like an ever-moving emery belt is rubbing swiftly back and forth upon a small section of the limpet's shell. Soon a small round well is bored through — the shell is perforated. Then a most horridly ingenious tool comes into play, a living pair of shears, on the end of a long mobile handle. This is pushed down upon the unfortunate limpet and actually begins to cut and hack it into small pieces. One by one these are sucked upward through the hole, and when the moon-snail packs up its outfit and moves away, it leaves a limpet shell, still ensconced in the rocky form, still a perfect shell except for the tiny round hole — but a shell without a limpet. The interior is thoroughly cleaned of every particle of the former owner.

As we watch the moon-snail glide smoothly on its way we observe that the long tentacles are never still — they forever ply here and there in the path to come. And we look in vain for eyes and suddenly realize that the moon-snail is blind. It feels its immediate way through life by touch, but its victims must be run down — I was going to say by a sense of smell, but in its watery element it is more correct to call it sense of taste.

My first memory of any snail is of long lines and curves of conch-shells along the walks and around the flower-beds belonging to my grandmother. In the days of the Great Queen that was considered the last word in landscape gardening. And it was a conch which led to my most cruel disillusionment — even worse than the passing of Santa Claus. I used secretly to grub up one of the garden conchs, hold it to my ear and, in spite of the downpour of soil, listen ecstatically to the sound of distant surf in the heart of the shell. The double joy of this was totally destroyed by some practical-minded servant or

219

gardener who showed me that a teacup gave forth identical moanings of the ancient seas.

When I found that a remarkable and very beautifully colored creature inhabited a conch shell and that in addition it made exceedingly delicious soup, my pain at its lack of accumulative, environmental sound-memory became alleviated. As a boy, when I began a collection of shells, I gave no more thought to the owners and makers than I did to the personality of the Knights who had worn the suits of armor in museum cases. I hardly put them in the category which fossils held in medieval philosophy — *lusus naturae*, acts of God, crystalline precipitates — but nevertheless they held places nearer my minerals than my insects.

One day I lay flat in my glass-bottomed boat drifting slowly across Castle Harbor to the north of Nonsuch. I was on the look-out for a reef favorable for diving, but suddenly my eye caught a well-marked trail ploughed through eel-grass four fathoms down. At the end of the furrow was a giant conch. We quickly heaved over the anchor and rigged the diving helmet. When I dropped down the ladder and began scouting around the eel-grass I found it was far from easy to locate the great shells. Their trails were lost in the low horizontal perspective and there were many small dead heads of coral which I picked up by mistake. At last, I located one and found it extremely heavy even under water. When I turned it over, the huge snail withdrew and rather amazingly squeezed out a bubble of air which, like a levitating pearl, rose slowly through the water. I tucked the creature under my arm and made for the ladder when I saw a second conch and put this beneath the other arm. As I was putting my foot on the lowest rung the surge threw me backward and I stepped inadvertently upon a third conch, the projections of which were so unpleasant that I dropped the first two. Miser-like, gathering them all up again, I began a one-sided ascent by means of feet, one knee and two fingers, with the trio clutched to me. The moment the conchs sensed one another they either blamed their present predicament upon each other, or the courage of three mollusteers together gave them courage to emerge from their shells and attack me. I know exactly how the Spartan youth felt with his irate fox, only I lacked the courage of that Greek Boy Scout and when my muscular snails began hacking at me I dropped them all. Again I tried and again I failed, for the punishing power of their sharp operculum was that of a claw of a sabre-toothed tiger, — their strength and activity were marvellous, and they tore through bathing suit and skin. Finally I succumbed to the humiliation of being beaten by three snails and carried them gingerly up, one at a time. This attack and defeat was my first real introduction to the architects and tenants of the shells, and it more than doubled my interest in this group of fellow organisms.

I have found that if I wait long enough, all the disappointments which I feel in natural things are proven to be merely the well deserved effects of conceit, yet in the great bountiness of Nature even this is not held against me. I unreasonably expected the roar of waves in the helix of the conch, and then the child's regret was partly swaged by other interests. As I near the end of this account of snails I hear in the distance, over the water, a low, sweet tone, swelling to penetrating power, a crescendo rise and fall and rise again, with a timbre and a certain quality which seems unlike that of any orchestral instrument. I unlimber my high power glasses and far out, toward the sunset, I pick up a fisherman's silhouette, standing in his boat, holding a conch shell to his lips. After he lowers the shell, the slow-moving trumpet sound again reaches my ears. And now my last sense of disappointment passes — I no longer regret my juvenile hopes, for the conch has yielded a sound, more intimately its own, more delightful because unexpected, than any pseudo roar of the surf could ever be.

And so we sum up our relations to snails; we recall that we put him in fables to personify lethargy; we eat him — gingerly and expensively and Gallically if he be a univalve, or wholesale and with gusto if he be within a hinged shelter. We risk life diving for him and hang the result of his diseases about the necks of fair women; when we are savages we chop up his shell and string it for money, and when a more advanced stage of civilization demands clothes, we dye them with royal Tyrian purple of snail's blood and hold them together with cunningly wrought rounded bits of nacre.

By far the best relationship, however, is when by association and attentive watching we have dipped deep into the personality of a snail, and by virtue of understanding can call him friend. I carry my remaining periwinkle — James — back to his wave-worn rock. He has given me three days of pleasure, has taught me considerable about himself and something I needed to know about my own being, and as a guest his life is safe — tabu. My laboratory table is again free and of my expedition into the world of snails there remains as material proof, only my artist's painting and a long-dried, glairy trail across a split infinitive.

CHAPTER XIV

A MOTHERLY KNIGHT IN ARMOR

THERE are three things of the sea which have been delineated by man more than any others — dolphins, mermaids, and seahorses, and there are three things about which we know almost less than any others — seahorses, mermaids and dolphins. I am sure that five thousand years ago some Egyptian or Chinaman or non-union stone mason of those days was daubing or hacking out an attempt at one or the other, and I know right well that at this very moment a young artist in a garret is drawing an original design of a pair of dolphins or seahorses with their tails entwined. I have awakened in a guest room where four walls revealed unending rows and columns of seahorses — so awful that I had to leap out of bed to avoid counting them and calculating how many more there would be if the window glass had been filled in.

I really believe we know more about mermaids than dolphins or seahorses, for there is a splendid freedom of imagination which is engendered by the uncertainty of existence of anything — a freedom cribbed and confined by knowledge of actuality. Our medieval ancestors believed much more in mermaids than in other marine organisms, and I am sure that if a mermaid and a seahorse appeared for the first time at the same instant I should be much more astonished at the latter.

My initial experience with a seahorse in Bermuda was from the point of a souvenir rather than as *Hippocampus punctulatus*. It was the first point of call of the Arcturus and we anchored at St. Georges in an afternoon's downpour of rain. I stayed only a few minutes on shore, went to a drugstore and bought the first thing I saw — a dried seahorse covered with gold paint. Had I left it, its future would probably have been to collect dust on the whatnot of some babbittian parlor, instead of which it performed a nobler function — that of a leavening climax after many hours of intensive investigation, in a sudden burst of amazement as Will Gregory saw a golden seahorse lying amid the scarlet and ebony treasures from a mile deep haul in the Sargassum Sea. This achieved successfully, it was thrown overboard and as it sank into the depth of mid-ocean I knew that the slow disintegration even of a dry and gilded seahorse would bring nourishment and joy of life to a host of diminutive scavengers, and then I remembered that my shilling was still on its way from one Bermudian hand or pocket to another, and I was pleased with the destiny of my first seahorse.

If we keep on thinking mermaid hard enough we will probably come across something not unlike such a lady and much more wonderful. Things work out that way quite often, as in the case of the sea-

NONSUCH

horse. When Aristotle and the poets of classical Greece wrote of Hippocampus they had in mind a wholly mythical sea-monster, a dragon, half horse and half fish. They thoroughly believed in this piscine-centaur and so there soon swam into their ken a half horse and half caterpillar and Hippocampus being only imaginarily " preoccupied " as our taxonomists would say, it naturally fitted the new natatory reality. Medicine evolving slowly, out of witch doctors and magic, and museums not yet having come in, any creature as strange as a seahorse would, in those early days, be considered from the point of view of drugs. So we find attributed to it a marvellous list of panaceas. If I had only had a library of early chirurgeons on the Arcturus and a little more faith I would not so readily have consigned my dried seahorse to the deep, but would have burned it and consumed its ashes in wine and thereby have guarded against pain-in-the-side, or, taken merely mixed with water, my canker and leprosy would have been alleviated. Best of all, had I stirred my Hippocampus ashes with oil of marjoram or liquid pitch and rubbed it on my bald pate a glorious head of hair would have resulted.

We may laugh at these prescriptions of old, but what except a feeling of shame shall we cherish toward an elaborate volume of seashore life, printed within three years, which states that Hippocampus is a primitive ganoid, that it lives to be a century old, and that it inhabits depths under great pressure! Before we ever smugly deride the ignorance or

226

credulity of our ancestors let us stop a moment and recite the phrase: " Remember Tennessee! " It is a mortifying but healthful exercise. To appreciate a seahorse to the full we must make ourselves believe that we are the first to discover it; the initial playing of the Rosary, or September Morn fresh from the artist's brush, and all that sort of thing.

We require a seahorse, so from Nonsuch we send out a motor boat and pull a small dredge slowly through some of the growth of eel-grass in Castle Harbor. One, two, three or no seahorses may result, but usually we find at least one of the curious little beings lying quietly in the mass of trigger-fish, shells, grass, seaweed and mud. He is as helpless as a prostrate knight in armor. I lift him and gently wash the mud out of his fin — mane, I was going to say — and then I let him slide down the submerged ways of my fingers and he is launched in a fresh aquarium. He rights himself — not like other fish, but vertically; turns his head from left to right, and glides slowly away. He seems to have no visible power of propulsion, but it is the invisibility of an airplane propellor — the fin on the back has become a dim, thin haze, its endless rippling web pushing back against the resisting water. The aquarium is a narrow rectangle and the seahorse traverses one long side, then a short end, and rests. And this first journey drives home a simile which needed just such an impetus; much more than the head of a horse, our Hippocampus resembles the knight of the chess-board, and his first move in the aquarium has been a knight's move — two squares ahead and one to the right.

It is well, however, to get rid of the horse idea altogether, and watch and learn to like our fish for himself. I put in a branch of seaweed and the long tail feels for it and coils about it with the grip of a chameleon. The next person who comes up to look cannot at first find the seahorse — he has begun to lose his identity. As we watch, this continues — he shifts from dusky brown to a pale neutral color and then again to dark, this time green, and Hippocampus is fairly within the protective cloak of seaweed sanctuary. He has gone vegetable and has taken upon himself the easy load of seaweed dangers and the very considerable advantage of algal immunity. I reach down and gently swing the weed back and forth, and still another trick is sprung — the little creature sways both body and head loosely to and fro in rhythm with what to him are the swells of ocean. On the tips of the knobs and spines of his armor are numerous, long bits of frayed-out filament, and these wave about and importantly diminish his zoölogical reality.

So here we have the seahorse and his niche in the world, balanced and weighed in the scales of life and death and found on the whole good. From snout to tail he is encased in bony jointed rings — one ring to each backbone, and while it slows him down almost to snail-pace, yet it serves to protect him from small predaceous crabs and other enemies. To carry about such a complete armor requires delicate ad-

justments, one of which is a large swim-bladder
filled with gas just sufficiently buoyant to hold him
in hydrostatic equilibrium. If, through accident, his
inner balloon is punctured and the merest pinpoint
of a gas bubble escapes, gravity seizes upon him, he
sinks helpless to the bottom, there to remain until
his wound be mended, or until nemesis comes along
on legs or fins.

Even for the seahorse in perfect health and
strength there are waiting scores of hungry mouths
armed with great cruel teeth which would crush him
like a nut. Against these he builds up the seaweed
defense — of haunt, color, pattern, shape, movement, and in addition he has even an unpleasant
odor — or, to water creatures, taste. His tail fin —
most valuable of all for progression — is gone and
instead he twines like a tendril. His life is lived at
lowest output of energy, a semi-sessile, pseudo-
crinoid or sorts, almost, we might think, on the way
to the fixation of barnacles. But this is not degen-
eration, it is adaptation to a safe environment, and
as we go on to study Hippocampus we realize that
he need have no envy for the swift herring or the
voracious dolphin.

It would seem that in the matter of food our seahorse must desert the quiet, patient, elementalness
of seaweed and dangerously revert to fish activity.
But here again Nature has worked out a most ingenious plan. For such a vegetative existence little
nourishment can be needed, yet we have a carnivore
which must have food. Resting on a frond of weed

NONSUCH

in the aquarium is a tiny crustacean, one of the untold myriads which inhabit all the seas in the world.
The seahorse has also seen the copepod, but he
wishes to keep me under surveillance as well. Slowly
he swims nearer and nearer, and peers ahead with
the comic intensity peculiar to short-sightedness.
He turns sideways, and now the approach is still
slower and he accomplishes two things simultaneously — one eye is cocked forward, gazing steadily
at his victim, the other is twisted far back, never
leaving our person. It was fairly disconcerting and
rather disturbed my own concentration. He throt-
tled down his little push propellor to lowest gear,
and the slowness of his advance began to approach
the rapidity of the growth of his seaweed. Then he
went into reverse, with no change that I could detect in fin ripples, and I looked and found that the
copepod had vanished. I was certain that it had not
swum away, the seahorse had made no snap or bite
in its direction, and I was completely confused.

It was a long time before I had another chance
to be in at the death after a seahorse's stalk and this
time I knew rather than saw what happened. It was
in a small hand aquarium and against the glass
floated a score or more of fish eggs which had come
in with a surface haul. I was lucky enough to get a
flat-field eight-diameter hand lens in position without causing the seahorse to shy. I watched without
a wink and I saw the mouth of Hippocampus open
wide, whereupon one egg after another simply was
no longer where it had been an instant before. A

flicker — and I knew that an egg had been sucked with amazing speed from a distance into the tube mouth but my senses were too dull, my rods and cones too human-slow to register such bullet speed. Then the reason for it flashed upon me and I saw how, even in its pursuit and capture of living prey, the seahorse still plays the rôle of a vegetable. The cheek of this fish is formed of one large bone, the opercle, and is fastened by strong muscles directly over the gill-openings. There are no clogging gill-rakers or teeth or tongue, so that a sudden lifting of this great pair of valves induces a mighty flux of water, sufficient to drag with it at lightning speed any living creature in the path of the waterspout.

I have never seen the courtship of seahorses, but it is described as most amusing, the marine stallion shaking his head and moving swiftly around the female. I was about to pen some light, casual phrase about all that was lacking was to have him paw the water and neigh, when I came across an account, which, as so often happens, made considerable sense out of a meaningless joke. For it is recorded that by cunning movements of the lower jaw the little fish can produce a loud snapping which increases in volume and frequency as the season of courtship approaches. They have even been known to call and answer one another when confined in separate aquariums.

We might reasonably suppose that now we had exhausted the little bag of life tricks of a seahorse: Remains only to record that the eggs are deposited and hatched, the young grow up and the eternal cycle starts another turn. But we are only at the beginning. Hippocampus is to prove that for sheer interest the last fact may be first, that a psychological reverse may make all physical shifts seem trivial; that what would be abnormal in ourselves has become usual and general in seahorses, and (what in science is almost a truism) that to the most dramatic phenomena we can ascribe no primary reasons or ultimate values.

We left the male seahorse doing his best to charm his mate, curvetting about, rippling his mane, snapping his jaws. The climax comes when she approaches and the two little creatures, rearing high, meet in mid-water. By the rules of sex throughout the ages at this moment the eggs should be fertilized, but apparently the race of seahorses is bound by no rules. At the moment of contact, one or several eggs pass from the ovary of the female out into the water, and by some instinctive bit of magic are slipped into the orifice of a pouch which, like the pocket of a kangaroo, is suspended in front of the male. What we mistook for evidences of an unusually heavy meal is something far otherwise. Again and again the female swims up, and egg after egg is produced and passed between them. So our generous male was wooing not only for marriage but for the custody and care of prospective children. The last egg is tucked away and without a cheerio or backward glance, the bride turns and swims off, to the work or play or meditation on life which occupy a lady

A MOTHERLY KNIGHT IN ARMOR

Hippocampus — I know not, after the amazing, ten-minute honeymoon whether to call her maid, wife or seahorse widow.

Also without a thanks-very-much, or even a well-merited sigh of envy of his more fortunate brothers in the world, our seahorse — etymologically a woman — swims off in his life's path, with his pocket full of the hope of the next generation.

If it is true that the eggs require four weeks to develop, then a fathom or two down, among the eel-grass and seaweeds of Castle Harbor a certain seahorse was courted, married and deserted on a Saturday night, the sixth of June. On the second of July we seined him off our bathing beach. As he glided gracefully about the aquarium I saw that he was a horse of unusual beauty. He was full grown — one hundred millimetres from snout to tail — or, less impressively, four inches. His color was a brilliant sea-green, darkened on the back, but the cheeks, chest and pouch aglow with this beautiful shade; his eyes were blazing gold, cut four square by lines of alabaster; his neck was arched and proud as that of a thoroughbred Arab. The pectoral fins were long and wide-spread like wings, and the graceful body gleamed with a host of white dots, streaming out into constellations or concentrated into galaxies — good reasons all for calling him Pegasus.

His pouch was greatly distended and now and then, even when he was quietly resting, the emerald surface was troubled, quivered, and was quiet again.

233

I returned frequently to the tank and watched him time after time make the circuit of the glass and back to his resting frond. He was restless and gave no time to feeding. His eyes kept turning, twisting, sometimes in rhythm or often independently as if they belonged to a span of horses. So I left him at midnight, slowly gliding on his rounds.

The following day, at ten o'clock, I saw the first seacolt break from the paternal stable and rush across the aquarium. I chivied it into a narrow glass and watched it carefully for a long time. Its activity was prodigious and its position was ancestral. Never for more than a moment did it rear into a true sea-horse posture, but was usually outstretched with tail trailing and head bent at only a few degrees, reminiscent of some pipefishlike forefather. Its heart beat vigorously and the great dorsal fin and the lower pectorals fanned the water and sent it swiftly ahead. The tail was the most amazing portion of its anatomy — it coiled and uncoiled, stretched and drew back, but especially it lashed from side to side. More than any other movement of fin or head or body, this lateral stroke was characteristic. When it wished to attain ultimate speed, it was by lateral wriggling, and when it began to resent and be enraged at the constant bumping of its nose against the glass it twisted its tail into a veritable corkscrew, then undid itself and with the greatest ease astonishingly entwined the tip around its own snout, neck and fin. Now and then it opened its tiny tube mouth, and the short, broad hyoid bone

would bend downward in an absurd resemblance to
a very blunt, second lower jaw.

At four o'clock two more young seahorses slipped
out of the opening of the pouch corral. This was
distended and throbbing with life — the pressure
and struggles of little heads and bodies being
plainly discernible on the surface as intermittent
dimples and bulges. A few minutes later a loud cry
arose from my watcher and an instant after with
my hand lens, I was at the aquarium.

The parent Hippocampus had taken a firm grip
with his tail around the branch of a seafern near
the bottom and was swaying back and forth with
head drawn in and the body and pouch pushed far
forward. As I watched, the body was drawn back,
and then, every muscle being brought into play, his
whole being again strained forward. The upper
third of the pouch which usually shows as a deep
fold down the middle was now distended to the full,
and in the center was revealed a small round orifice.
As the pouch reached its utmost distention the
opening enlarged slightly and with a convulsive
movement there was ejected a mass, a mist, a whole
herd of young. They were thrown out into the
world in the shape of a rounded ball, which, like a
smoke-ring or a bomb from a firework, held together
as it moved rapidly upward and obliquely forward
through the water. Only when it began to lose impetus ten or twelve inches away, did it spray out
into long streamers and scattered blobs of infant
Pegasi. From the moment of slackened paternal

impulse the individual seahorse motes assumed individual activity, swimming, twining their tails around themselves and one another, lashing out from side to side for all the world like diminutive crocodiles. With all this casual indirective movement there was a steady stampede of each successive herd toward the surface; as a scientist I would describe it as positively phototropic.

Five more parental HE explosions took place before the pouch was empty, and the fourth and fifth were both still ball-like, revolving slowly upward, while the earlier ones had spread out into a subsurface film of frisking young Hippocampi.

The pouch did not collapse as I expected it would, but for another half-hour was only slightly shrunken. Yet the last of the young had emerged — three hundred and six in all. This was the end, and in the morning the parent's pouch was indistinguishable and the green color had given way to a suit of dark brown, starred with white and faced with yellow-green. And father and young were doing well.

The story was once told and has been repeated many times of how the young seahorses return, at the approach of danger, to their father's pouch. It is a charming idea but is quite untrue. There is no bond between offspring and parent once they are shot out of his pocket, and their instinct to swim up to the surface and toward the light is wholly unlike his ideas of a proper trajectory — which is down and among the protective fronds of seaweed. In addition to this the opening of the pouch closes tightly immediately after the multiple births, and precludes any readmission.

There is no doubt about the interest which the life of a dolphin must hold, and I am sure that the way of a mermaid in the sea would inspire a best seller, but for charm, for quiet success in life and for sheer unexpectedness of mating, incubation and birth the seahorse has no equal. As to the questions which arise: How did this intricate and reversed relationship first come about? Why does the female hand over her eggs? Why does the male parent shelter and incubate them? Why . . . I can only answer, I don't know.

CHAPTER XV

I SHOULD like to compose a few paragraphs about a fish known as *Atherina,* and to make certain that my audience is undeceived and interested I will say in the first place that its extreme length and weight are two and a half inches and one and one-third grams (loud scuffling of feet dying out in the distance as Isaac Walton and his followers leave); it has been known for one hundred and seventy-five years and is extremely common (exit the clique of taxonomists); its name is from the Greek ἄθεριν and is very appropriate, meaning Little Arrow (feeble applause from the single etymologist present); throughout historical times it has been considered such delicious eating that it has generally been called Fishes of the King (out go the soviets and their friends and relations, their heavy tread made inaudible by thunderous applause from gentlefolk gourmands). I must state that I know but little of the cause of the schooling habits of this fish (hand-clapping from all honest men left); and here I will read two sentences from the most recent brochure on this subject (contented sounds from a bibliophile who got in by accident):

" In the case of the inherent reactions of any organism the simple elements must be considered in their coördination with each other and their subordination to the whole to a far greater extent than in the study of the merely structural morphology, as almost any one of the many instincts centered around the various stimulations to which the organism is able to respond may temporarily or permanently serve to suppress the manifestations of any or all of the other complexes in the nervous organization of the species, or may equally serve to increase their external effect. . . . In discussing the occurrence and varying development of the schooling behavior of the different forms we must therefore not only observe the external manifestations of the schooling instinct, but we must also consider the possibility of these manifestations having been altered, promoted, reduced or even entirely suppressed by the interference of other compatible or incompatible instincts in the psychological make-up of the species considered." Here, in two sentences and one hundred and sixty words, we have one modern method of attack on the subject, and at this point, I myself leave in search of a more direct, simple approach. I go down to the ancient wreck which is my Nonsuch breakwater, and, lying prone on the hot planks, focus my low power glasses on the milling school which I knew I should find there.

Many years ago while watching great numbers of wading birds on the shores of Lake Chapala in Mexico, I was first struck by the strange unanimity of birds in flight — what I called the spirit of the

239

flock. Since then I have had long talks with William
Morton Wheeler about the same idea in regard to
the actions of an army or a nest of ants. Now that
I am attempting to learn something about the ways
of fishes I have many times watched their schooling
habits.

A few feet away from me was a concentrated
school of small fish. When they were drawn out
into a long ribbon I counted fifty, and a conservative estimate of the whole was fourteen hundred —
and this was an extremely small school, as schools
of Little Arrows go. Slowly the school swung first
in one, and then in the opposite direction, it changed
from a circle to a dumb-bell, to beads on a string, to
a crescent, and now and then I halved it momentarily, when it rejoined and became some unnamed
figure. It had length, breadth, and depth, intentions,
achievement, attempt, refusal, impetus — but one
never thought of individual units. As I watched, it
became more and more a sentient individual, with
particular desires and activities; in the little harbor
beneath me were snappers, and squirrelfish, cowfish
and bream and — it. It kept half-way from the
bottom, and its shadow on the bottom was the veri-
similitude of a slow creeping worm, which flowed
over pebbles, reached fingers out sideways, drew
back and then slipped out of sight, as the sun went
under a cloud.

I could do strange things with this Atherina organism — like boring three holes at once through
it. I waited until it became a broad oval and then

tossed three tiny pebbles simultaneously. As they sank, there opened beneath each of them a round hole, and soon they all dropped through three separate wells and the trio of apertures closed up again. There was no especial fright, simply a very reasonable withdrawing from the unusual phenomenon of pebbles dropping from the sky.

In the dark hull of the Sea-Fern wreck on which I was lying there were a number of Little Arrows or Silversides and I captured and imprisoned one in a narrow hand aquarium. Atherina is a perfectly good little fish and once seen he will never be forgotten, but to put an adequate and easily visualized description of him on paper is most difficult. He is long and minnow-shaped, with a broad band along the side of glittering silver tinsel, a small mouth and a huge eye. That is the rough elevation, the blueprint sketch, but gives no idea of the delicacy of the turquoise-green back, which, in a certain angle of the sun, shifts to molten silver, the unnamed blue of the head, the wonderful little branched color-cells which set off his fins and tail, and finally the cold silver of the great eye. The eye alone shows the Little Arrows to be creatures of fear, and they are set, like those of a rabbit, on the very sides of the head, looking behind as well as sideways — the eye of a pursued, not of a pursuer in life's race. So large are these eyes that ten of them would cover the entire surface of one side of the fish, to compare with which a man's eyes would have to measure six inches across.

NONSUCH

Except for minor details my description will cover the general appearance of all Silversides in the world. Wherever they live, they are found in shallow water and in great schools. Now human beings, being complex beyond all necessity, have scores of reasons for collecting in schools — our word school is only one of the many — we call them audiences, clubs, congregations, passengers, tourists, armies and mobs — associated for education, society, religion, transportation, defense and discontent or anger. Fish, being so busy living their life to the full, have less time to worry about casual things, and have no trenches or cyclone cellars, nor does the future interest them, so they have no meeting houses or churches, and no fish ever joined another fish because of anger; mobs are the prerogative of human beings.

One way of finding out about anything is to discover when it does not exist; in Bermuda there are three things which preclude schooling of the Silversides — extreme youth, night and the mackerel season. The primary object of schooling is probably rather a primitive one. It is true throughout the animal kingdom that the creatures which live in herds or flocks are usually inferior in intellect. Wasps and bees are clever insects but the solitary wasps are geniuses in comparison. In an aquarium the gregarious fishes are deadly dull, eternally milling about in circles, whereas those living solitarily or in pairs well repay watching, especially in their native haunts.

242

THE SCHOOLS OF LITTLE ARROWS

The young of Silversides have their fling at sea, drifting about on the surface after hatching, far off shore. I have taken them in surface hauls as far out as three miles, but singly, with no hint of gregariousness.

The nocturnal dissolving of a school is a very delicately balanced phenomenon. Twice I have been watching schools of small fry on a hot, sunny day when a dark thunder cloud suddenly obscured the sky. Automatically, as if they were chemical molecules acted upon by some powerful reagent, the mass loosened, a few even frayed out, six in one group began snapping at some prey invisible to me. On the first occasion the rain began to come down in sheets and completely blotted out my submarine view. The second time, the storm did not materialise, the sun reappeared and the strayed atoms gathered close once more. With sundown comes the slackening of this schooling instinct and when I light a submarine light, the Silversides come casually, in ones or twos. Feeding probably goes on at night, as during the day, for hour after hour, not the slightest attempt is made by the thousands to capture food.

Bermuda fishermen tell how these little fish keep together for a week or two after the mackerel arrive, and it is then that we can see the two kinds of gregarious fish in full action — the one pursuing, the other fleeing — each to the limit of its power. But before long terror of their voracious enemies becomes so great that the Silversides

243

hide for the remaining month of the mackerels' stay.

There are about thirty species of Little Arrows in the world. They are eminently successful fishlets and abound in every favorable bit of shallow tropical water from Bermuda to Panama, Norway to South Africa, Japan and the East Indies to Australia. In Haiti my motorboat sometimes passed through a school for a mile or more without a break — a solid, concentrated mass of silvery motes sliding along below the surface, sometimes many yards deep. When we consider the millions of fish in one such school, the thought of the numbers of *Atherina* in all seven seas becomes comparable only with astronomical figures. The genus *Atherina* has a fairly respectable pedigree, for we have found a large-headed fossil member, very slightly changed from the Arrows of today, which swam and doubtless schooled fifty millions of years ago.

If we were Atherinas, and living in a world whose men and birds and fish preferred *Atherina* to other diet, it would seem much better if we skulked alone or with a single fish friend near the crevices of rocks and the kindly sanctuary of seaweed, instead of advertising our abundance by foregathering in conspicuous multitudes. Unlike muskoxen, whose strongest defenders face outwards in a hollow square, the outermost Little Arrow is only nearest to the maw of the first approaching enemy. If, again, I was one of a great school, my dominant instinct would be to bore through to the very heart, hoping that impending appetites would be satisfied by the dozens of my outermost brethren. Yet I have never seen any such movement on the part of the members of the "skin" layer of the schooling organism.

A fairly good index to the dangers which threaten a creature is the number of its eggs. A mouse, a quail and a codfish must produce unusually large numbers of eggs or offspring to balance the great mortality which rages among eggs and young. Yet Little Arrows instead of depositing half a dozen million like the codfish, or even a paltry five hundred thousand as the mackerel does, produces only two or three hundred eggs, several times a year. There must be some amply protective circumstances of which we are wholly ignorant, which stand between *Atherina* and the need for greater prolificness.

The eggs are covered with a scanty growth of fine, long hairs, and these become entangled in the first bit of weed or coral they touch. For ten or twelve days they are safely anchored, and the young fish then emerges and becomes a wanderer on the face of the waters. After a few months those that are still alive begin to feel the call of the society of their brethren and of the shore, and little by little work in from the open sea, and form the kindergarten school of Little Arrows.

In every country where I have studied Atherinas, their food has been catholic in extent. They seem to refuse nothing that is of animal matter and swallowable — tiny worms, crustacea, eggs (often their own), bits of seaweed with attached organisms, diatoms and unnamable larvae. But insects are the favorite, and probably few are blown or fall off the cliffs or rocks which escape the sharp eyes of the Little Arrows. On Nonsuch an introduced species of European ant is found in myriads. Nowhere in the tropics have I found ants more abundant as individuals. During a southwest wind I have seined on opposite sides of the island and found only two ants in a dozen stomachs of fish taken on the windward side, while the tiny silvery maws of those on the northeastern or leeward side, were crammed with workers of the ants. I am quite sure that, given a single specimen taken close inshore on Nonsuch, from the contents of its stomach I could deduce the direction of the prevailing wind and the location of the school.

It is a dangerous thing to read human names of emotions or intentions into the actions of animals, but if it is done with deliberate desire only to point the fact, it is harmless. Fear and terror indeed, are responses which can safely be said to be common both to human beings and to animals. I lie and watch my school of Silversides, and test them in many ways. There is no question of the dominance of eyes in their life. A pebble dropped, as I have said, cuts a temporary notch or bores a hole in the school. A bit of wood thrown across the little bay causes the hundreds to dodge down several inches toward the bottom. But another sense — corresponding to our ear, is also at hair-trigger, ready to help. I strike iron against iron out of their sight on the deck, and the school swerves half a foot. Two boats bump gently together on the other side, and the school swings toward me with a single, flinching impulse.

Scattered through the hosts of *Atherina* are several score of a quite unrelated species — a round-bodied herringlet with a silver stripe, but with the terrible name of *Jenkinsia*. No matter how wonderful a professor of physiology Dr. Oliver Peebles Jenkins and how splendid a man — I resent the name of anyone of my race being given to the genus of a brave, individual, end-product member of the wild fauna of our globe. Having rid myself of this spot of "quarrelsome interest," I say hurrah for Jenkins, and return to the scores of his namesakes swimming before me.

On the surface, isolated, for reasons known only to themselves, was a school of thirteen of these herringlets. They represented the essence of fear — never quiet for a moment, turning, twisting, back, forth and around, as they saw, heard or imagined they detected danger. Little by little I increased this by a judicial rain of pebbles, until a handful sent them diving headlong into the school of Atherinas. They vanished, as a shadow merges with shade. Where they entered the surrounding members of the school fluttered for a moment and then quieted, in tune with the rest. Then from near the front end (for at that moment ' it ' had a front end)

there shot out thirteen fish, which rushed to the surface and began their eternal dashing and counter-
dashing. I knew my thirteen, for one was larger than
the rest, one had a sore shoulder, two were very dark
and one had a damaged tail. So there seemed to be
a tempo of terror among these fish — a degree of
fear which was not assuaged by immersion among
a quieter crowd of its fellows, but which drove it out
again, as an explosion of rage will agitate another
type of organism for awhile and then leave it. And
so, little by little, we might build up the psychology
of this composite Being of fish, this Corpuscular
School which deserves to be a singular, capitalized,
personal noun.

Play, among animals, is a much less certain subject than fear, for what to us appears complete relaxation may be far otherwise. Domestic animals
most certainly play, and it is difficult to ascribe
more serious motives to the occasional non-courtship,
non-feeding activities of dolphins, as well as the
apparent delight they take in swimming in the
forward push of water at the bow of a steamer.

With a quiet school of Silversides, a wooden
match and a calm, cloudy day I can magic play out
of the usually serious, preoccupied little fish. A
sinking pebble bores through them, as I have said,
but a small splinter of wood or match thrown on
the surface above the school has almost no effect.
A few, directly beneath, may flinch slightly, but
after a minute one, two, several, will drift up to the
bit of wood and begin to leap over it. First one,

then another goes over the hurdle, from this side or that, sometimes balking at the start and swimming away, more often flinching sideways, a leap clear of the surface, but very unlike the high, forward course when fleeing for life from an impi of mackerel. This may accomplish some real purpose, either practice or achievement, to which we have no clue, but as far as appearances go, it is sheer exuberance, relaxation, a momentary forgetting of the myriad dangers which menace even these favored fishes of the king from above, below and around, day and night, from birth to death.

Two memories I like, now and then, to take down from my *Atherina* archives, relive, and replace in the full knowledge that no experience more dramatic or dangerous or spectacular, in past life or to come, can ever obliterate them.

A day in early September, clear and warm, the air transparent and so quiet that the sea was like watered silk. On land the only life was a pair of bluebirds warbling so low to themselves that the sound barely detached itself from the silence. On the beach beneath a trio of turnstones butted against the piled windrows of sargassum, and a kingfisher looped from one headland to another. I sat on a high cliff and watched four separate schools of Silversides leap time after time into the air. Usually the hosts of pursuers simply boiled in their wake, but now and then a mackerel hurled himself a full yard after them, turning a somersault as if in play as much as in hunger.

NONSUCH

It was an amazing spectacle to see the ceiling of the water, apparently quite solid in its smoothness, suddenly troubled by an upward rain of thousands of living atoms, among which sinister, silvery sickles and boomerangs twisted and fell. In the distance the leaping fry looked like a myriad gleaming crescent moons which rose only to set in the same movement. Now and then, a great snout or fin would be poked slowly up into view suggesting unbelievable, invisible length behind.

I watched, fascinated, the breathlessness and calm shattered by the agonized life-and-death rush; the peace of mirrored water broken by the instant return of thousands of living dynamos, with every power of brain and body concentrated upon sheer speed. Time and time again this recurred, until there seemed a terrible rhythm to it all.

Then the silence, which the bluebirds had only enhanced, was shattered. From high overhead, a hard, metallic rattle cracked like the beginning of thunder, and the kingfisher set his wings to broad-arrow-barb shape and dropped straight into a curving wave of Silversides, turned, rose, and flew with deep notched loops to a rocky perch. With my glass I could see at least three of the small fish crosswise in his stout beak.

When I looked back, the performance was over: The mirror was blurred with the breath of a cats-paw of wind, the mackerel had gone where mackerel go after feeding and the ocean had taken again to itself hundreds of thousands of little fish — each with ideas, activities, hopes and fears of its own, but somehow subservient to the Spirit of the School.

On another day I slipped over the gunwale of my boat and down to a shallow sandy bottom three fathoms below the surface, close to an outlying islet near Nonsuch. There had been no recent storms nor heavy swells and the water was clear. Yet when I looked toward the abrupt rise of seaweed-covered rocks which marked the rim of the island, all was foggy and dim. I walked closer and saw that between me and the under shore there hung a dense veil of tens or hundreds of thousands of Silversides, all facing one way, all balanced in mid-water, each fish hardly a fin's reach apart from his fellows. As I approached, there appeared a tiny rent in the great blue-grey curtain — a frayed place in front of my helmet. There was no panic, no sustained fright as I came near, just a slow, hardly perceptible parting. And the strange thing was that this seemed to cause no crowding; it was as if the entire living portière swung slightly to one side. I went closer and an oval window opened silently — through which I could clearly see the seaweed and the little yellow wrasse beyond. I stepped back and the grey blinds were drawn together again, and I was again shut off by the solid wall of fish.

I now slipped off one of my four weights and cached it where I could not help but find it again. Then I took several steps ahead, and leaped with all my might. Of course the result was all slow motion, as it has to be under water. I left the sand

and rose up and forward, soaring slowly through the water, and before I began to sink I passed cleanly through the school — through a great oval window, with a sinuous crack overhead marking the track of the hose. There were fish in myriads above, on all sides and beneath me. I caught hold of an out-jutting crag far up the steep, submarine slope of the islet, and twisted quickly around in time to see the window narrow to a tall loop-hole, contract to a slit, and then mend itself — a living tapestry more beautiful than any fashioned on human looms, or imagined in any fairy tale of old.

Before we have the complete solution of the whys and wherefores of herding and flocking and school-ing, there must be a great deal of uncomfortable climbing and diving, hiding in unpleasant places, getting wet and hot and cramped and weary. And then, after we have tried to be sandpipers and ants, silversides and mackerel, we may attain to the honor of such knowledge as our prejudiced, but humbled minds will permit.

TEXT IDENTIFICATIONS

253

TEXT IDENTIFICATIONS

TEXT IDENTIFICATIONS

ILLUSTRATION IDENTIFICATIONS

INDEX

INDEX

INDEX